CROSSWORDS WORD SEARCHES
LOGIC PUZZLES & SURPRISES!

mind STRETCHERS

SAFFRON EDITION

EDITED BY ALLEN D. BRAGDON

Reader's Digest

The Reader's Digest Association, Inc.
New York / Montreal

Project Staff

PROJECT EDITOR
Robert Ronald

PUZZLE EDITOR
Allen D. Bragdon

PRINCIPAL PUZZLE AUTHORS
Peter De Schepper
Frank Coussement
John M. Samson
Sam Bellotto Jr.

CONTRIBUTING PUZZLE AUTHOR
Ron Grosset

SERIES ART DIRECTOR
Andrée Payette

DESIGNER
Craig Brown

PRODUCTION ARTIST
Chris A. Cant

ILLUSTRATIONS
BrainSnack®

COPY EDITOR
Judy Yelon

PROOFREADER
Penny Grearson

MANAGER, ENGLISH BOOK EDITORIAL
Pamela Johnson

VICE PRESIDENT, BOOK EDITORIAL
Robert Goyette

The Reader's Digest Association, Inc.

PRESIDENT AND CHIEF EXECUTIVE OFFICER
Robert Guth

EXECUTIVE VICE PRESIDENT, RDA & PRESIDENT, NORTH AMERICA
Dan Lagani

EXECUTIVE VICE PRESIDENT, RDA & PRESIDENT, ALLRECIPES.COM
Lisa Sharples

EXECUTIVE VICE PRESIDENT, RDA & PRESIDENT, EUROPE
Dawn Zier

ISBN 978-1-55475-104-4

Address any comments about *Mind Stretchers, Saffron Edition* to:

Reader's Digest Association (Canada) ULC
Book Series Editor
1100 Rene-Levesque Blvd. West
Montreal, Quebec H3B 5H5
Canada

To order copies of this or other editions of the *Mind Stretchers* book series,
call 1-800-846-2100 in the United States and 1-800-465-0780 in Canada.

Visit us on the Web, in the United States at **rd.com**
and in Canada at **readersdigest.ca**

Printed in the United States of America

Contents

Dear Puzzler,

If you have ever been entertained by a ventriloquist and a dummy, you may have been tricked into thinking, if only for a moment or two, that the dummy was actually speaking.

While the ventriloquist effect depends upon the performer's ability to create the illusion he's "throwing his voice," it also involves something more complex that takes place within the brain of the viewer. Studies reveal that ventriloquism, the phenomenon of inaccurately thinking a voice is coming from a spatially displaced source, is due to the way the brain perceives and integrates sights and sounds.

Researchers David Alais and David Burr, tested the ventriloquist effect by using brief light "blobs" and sound "clicks." Subjects were asked to locate the spatial position of these blobs and clicks. The stimuli were first presented separately, and observers had to indicate which of the stimuli, light or sound, appeared more to the left of a given area. Next, blobs and clicks were presented simultaneously in one of two ways: spatially displaced from each other, and equally displaced to the left or right of a specified point.

Results showed that the ability to locate the auditory or visual stimuli depended upon the size and intensity of the visual stimulus. For instance, if the light was bright and easy to locate, subjects tended to report the sound "click" as closer to or in the same location as the light. Thus, vision dominated or "captured" sound. On the other hand, if the light was weak, blurred, and its location hard to distinguish, the reverse was true; subjects reported the light as closer to the correct location of the click. In cases where light and sound were presented at the same time and position in space, subjects were much more likely to identify the correct location than when a stimulus was singularly presented.

You can test part of this theory while sitting in front of a cinema screen or television set. When watching a movie, it is easy to believe the actor's voice, the screeching car or exploding gun is coming from what you see on the screen. In fact, since the visual stimulus overrides the auditory, the sound merges with the visual effects. If, however, the screen should go blurry or the picture disappeared, you would become fully aware of the soundtrack and its real location emanating from the speakers.

Thus, the brain is an instrument that can unite incoming visual and auditory data to determine spatial location, but integration is not always accurate, and in fact, it is often flawed. Since a strong visual stimulus takes precedence over sound, it can distort our perceived location of a sound, explaining why you may one day, if you have not already, find yourself listening to a dummy.

So beware—all is not always what it seems! Our BrainSnack puzzles in this Mind Stretchers volume are testing you. Concentrate and don't be a dummy!

Allen D. Bragdon

Mind Stretchers Puzzle Editor

■ Meet the Authors

Allen D. Bragdon

Allen describes himself as "the whimsical old dog with puzzle experience and a curious mind." He is a member of the Society for Neuroscience, founding editor of *Games* magazine and editor of the Playspace daily puzzle column, formerly syndicated internationally by *The New York Times*. The author of dozens of books of professional and academic examinations and how-to instructions in practical skills, Allen is also the director of the Brainwaves Center.

PeterFrank

PeterFrank was founded in 2000. It is a partnership between High Performance bvba, owned by Peter De Schepper, and Frank Coussement bvba, owned by Frank Coussement. Together they form a dynamic, full-service content provider specialized in media content.They have more than twenty years of experience in publishing management, art/design and software development for newspapers, consumer magazines, special interest publications and new media.

John M. Samson

John M. Samson is currently editor of Simon & Schuster's *Mega Crossword Series*. His crosswords have appeared on cereal boxes, rock album covers, quilts, jigsaw puzzles, posters, advertisements, newspapers, magazines ... and sides of buildings. John also enjoys painting and writing for the stage and screen.

Sam Bellotto Jr.

Sam Bellotto Jr. has been making puzzles professionally since 1979, when he broke into the business by placing his first sale with *The New York Times Magazine* under then crossword puzzle editor Eugene T. Maleska. Sam has been a regular contributor to Simon & Schuster, *The New York Times*, Random House, and magazines such as *Back Stage*, *Central New York*, *Public Citizen* and *Music Alive!* Bellotto's Rochester, NY-based company, Crossdown, develops word-puzzle computer games and crossword construction software.

When Sam is not puzzling he's out hiking with Petra, his black Labrador dog.

BrainSnack®

The internationally registered trademark BrainSnack® stands for challenging, language-independent, logical puzzles and mind games for kids, young adults and adults. The brand stands for high-quality puzzles. Whether they are made by hand, such as visual puzzles, or generated by a computer, such as sudoku, all puzzles are tested by the target group they are made for before they are made available. In order to guarantee that computer-generated puzzles can actually be solved by humans, BrainSnack® makes programs that only use human logic algorithms.

◾ Meet the Puzzles

Mind Stretchers is filled with a delightful mix of classic and new puzzle types. To help you get started, here are instructions, tips and examples for each.

WORD GAMES

Crossword Puzzles

Clues. Clues. Clues.

Clues are the deciding factor that determines crossword-solving difficulty. Many solvers mistakenly think strange and unusual words are what make a puzzle challenging. In reality, crossword constructors generally try to avoid grid esoterica, opting for familiar words and expressions.

For example, here are some actual clues you'll be encountering and their respective difficulty levels:

LEVEL 1	Florida key
LEVEL 2	Surly
LEVEL 3	Emperor Selassie
LEVEL 4	Omani coin
LEVEL 5	Perrier in *Murder by Death*

Clues to amuse. Clues to educate. Clues to challenge your mind.

All the clues are there—what's needed now is your answers.

Happy solving!

Word Searches

by PeterFrank

Both kids and grownups love 'em, making word searches one of the most popular types of puzzle. In a word search, the challenge is to find hidden words within a grid of letters. In the typical puzzle, words can be found in vertical columns, horizontal rows or along diagonals, with the letters of the words running either forward or backward. You'll be given a list of words to find. But it does not stop there. There is a hidden message—related to the theme of the word search—in the letters left behind after all of the clues have been found. String together those extra letters, and the message will reveal itself.

Hints: *One of the most reliable and efficient searching methods is to scan each row from top to bottom for the first letter of the word. So if you are looking for "violin," you would look for the letter "v." When you find one, look at all the letters that surround it for the second letter of the word (in this case, "i"). Each time you find a correct two-letter combination (in this case, "vi"), you can then scan either for the correct three-letter combination ("vio") or the whole word.*

Word Sudoku

by PeterFrank

Sudoku puzzles have become hugely popular, and our word sudoku puzzles bring a much-loved challenge to word puzzlers.

The basic sudoku puzzle is a 9 x 9 square grid, split into 9 square regions, each containing 9 cells. You need to complete the grid so that each row, each column and each 3 x 3 frame contains the nine letters from the black box above the grid.

There is always a hidden nine-letter word in the diagonal from top left to bottom right.

EXAMPLE   SOLUTION

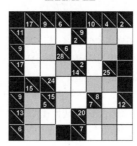

NUMBER GAMES

Sudoku

by PeterFrank

The original sudoku number format is amazingly popular the world over due to its simplicity and challenge.

The basic sudoku puzzle is a 9 x 9 square grid, split into 9 square regions, each containing 9 cells. Complete the grid so that each row, each column and each 3 x 3 frame contains every number from 1 to 9.

EXAMPLE   SOLUTION

As well as classic sudoku puzzles, you'll also find sudoku X puzzles, where the main diagonals must also include every number from 1 to 9, and sudoku twins with two overlapping grids.

Kakuro

by PeterFrank

These puzzles are like crosswords with numbers. There are clues across and down, but the clues are numbers. The solution is a sum which adds up to the clue number.

Each number in a black area is the sum of the numbers that you have to enter in the empty boxes beside or below. The empty boxes that make up the sum are called a run. The sum of the across run is written above the diagonal in the black area, while the sum of the down run is written below the diagonal.

Runs can contain only the numbers 1 through 9, and each number in a run can only be used once. The gray boxes contain only odd numbers and the white contain only even numbers.

EXAMPLE   SOLUTION

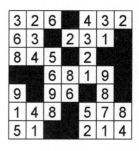

LOGIC PUZZLES

Binairo

by PeterFrank

Binairo puzzles look similar to sudoku puzzles. They are just as simple and challenging but that is where the similarity ends.

There are two versions: odd and even. The even puzzles feature a 12 x 12 grid. You need to complete the grid with zeros and ones, until there are 6 zeros and 6 ones in every row and every column. No more than two of the same number can be next to or under each other. Rows or columns with exactly the same combination are not allowed.

EXAMPLE   SOLUTION

The odd puzzles feature an 11 x 11 grid. You need to complete the grid with zeros and ones until there are 5 zeros and 6 ones in every row and column.

Keep Going

In this puzzle, start on a blank square of your choice and connect as many blank squares as possible with one single continuous line.

You can only connect squares along vertical and horizontal lines, not along diagonals. You must continue the connecting line up until the next obstacle—i.e., the rim of the box, a black square or a square that has already been used.

You can change direction at any obstacle you meet. Each square can only be used once. The number of blank squares left unused is marked in the upper square. There is more than one solution, but we include only one solution in our answer key.

EXAMPLE   SOLUTION

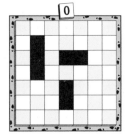 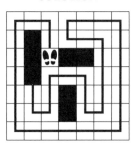

Number Cluster

by PeterFrank

Number Cluster puzzles are language-free, logical numerical problems. They consist of cubes on a 6 x 6 grid. Numbers have been placed in some of the cubes, while the rest are empty. Your challenge is to complete the grid by creating runs of the same number and length as the number supplied. So where a cube with the number 5 has been included on the grid, you need to create a run of five number 5's, including the cube already shown. The run can be horizontal, vertical, or both horizontal and vertical.

EXAMPLE   SOLUTION

Word Pyramid

Each word in the pyramid has the letters of the word above it, plus a new letter.

Start with the answer to No.1 and work your way to the base of the pyramid to complete the word pyramid.

Sport Maze

This puzzle is presented on a 6 x 6 grid. Your starting point is indicated by a red cell with a ball and a number. Your objective is to draw the shortest route from the ball to the goal, the only square without a number. You can only move along vertical and horizontal lines, but not along diagonals. The figure on each square indicates the number of squares the ball must be moved in the same direction. You can change direction at each stop.

EXAMPLE   SOLUTION

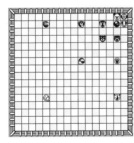

Cage the Animals

This puzzle presents you with a zoo divided into a 16 x 16 grid. The different animals on the grid need to be separated. Draw lines that will completely divide up the grid into smaller squares, with exactly one animal per square. The squares should not overlap.

EXAMPLE   SOLUTION

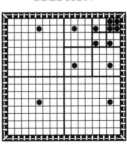

Throughout *Mind Stretchers* you will find unique stumpers, visual conundrums and other colorful challenges. Each comes with a new name and unique instructions. Our best advice? Patience and perseverance. Your eyes will need time to unravel the visual secrets.

BrainSnack® Puzzles

To solve a BrainSnack® puzzle, you must think logically. You'll need to use one or several strategies to detect direction, differences and/or similarities, associations, calculations, order, spatial insight, colors, quantities and distances. A BrainSnack® ensures that all the brain's capacities are fully engaged. These are brain sports at their best!

Sunny Weather

We all want to know the weather forecast, and here's your chance to figure it out! Arrows are scattered on a grid. Each arrow points toward a space where a sun symbol should be, but the symbols cannot be next to each other vertically, horizontally or diagonally. A symbol cannot be placed on top of an arrow. You must determine where the symbols should be placed.

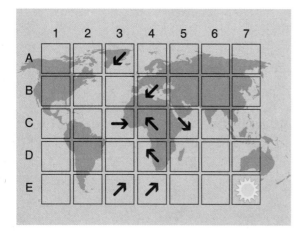

BRAINTEASERS

You'll also find more than 100 short brain-teasers scattered throughout these pages. These puzzles, found at the bottom of the page, will give you a little light relief from the more intense puzzles while still challenging you.

• ONE LETTER LESS OR MORE

• LETTERBLOCKS

• BLOCK ANAGRAM

SHADY OIL *(leisure time away from work)*

					A	

• DOODLE PUZZLE

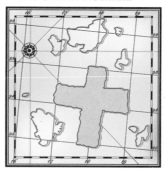

But wait—there's more!

There are additional brainteasers at the top of odd numbered pages, organized into two categories:

• **QUICK!:** These tests challenge your ability to instantly calculate numbers or recall well-known facts.

• **DO YOU KNOW...:** These more demanding questions probe the depth of your knowledge of facts and trivia.

■ Master Class:

You Must Remember This...

There are good memories, and then there is good memory

You may hear someone say, "I have a bad memory for dates," but never, "I have a bad memory for traumatic experiences." That's because memory is not a single skill or ability.

In fact there are many different memory systems and faculties and, therefore, many definitions of memory. Remembering where you left your car keys, and how to ride a bike are examples of discrete memory systems, and each resides in a different part of the brain. Phobias and post-traumatic stress disorder rely on yet other memory systems. While they all share certain elements, each developed at different evolutionary stages for distinctive reasons.

When we use the word "memory," we usually mean various memorizing abilities that are mostly conscious acts, a subset that includes memory for facts (semantic memory), and for events and places (episodic memory). Together, semantic memory and episodic memory are called declarative memory, and it is declarative memory people are referring to when they say they are good or bad at remembering things.

But are some people statistically better at remembering things than others?

Will it always be Dagwood who forgets the Bumstead wedding anniversary date, and never Blondie?

Superficial similarities between the sexes mask underlying differences

On a variety of experimental tests, men and women are about the same at remembering unfamiliar odors, or abstract images. But women outscore men at remembering words, stories, pictures, faces, and the locations of objects. What accounts for these gender similarities and differences?

Women are better at remembering things that are easy to "tag" or represent in words than they are at remembering things for which it is harder to attach a verbal label. So women's superiority at remembering certain things may be due to superior verbal skills, useful for both committing information to and retrieving knowledge from memory.

Then again, female superiority also may be due to some faculty that lies beyond verbal and memory skills per se—the ability to access categorized learned information more rapidly, for example. Studies supporting this interpretation show that gender differences in brain activity patterns during the act of retrieving information, most particularly in the function of frontal lobe brain regions, which play a role in accessing information efficiently and effectively.

The mind's ears and eyes

The frontal lobes play a particularly important role in yet another kind of memory called working memory (WM), a cognitive tool useful for a wide range of problem-solving tasks. It is usually defined as a very short-term memory storage system that helps you to hold information in your mind just long enough for immediate use.

If you add 12 and 14 in your head, it is WM that lets you remember the numbers to be added long enough for you to perform the necessary calculations to get the answer. For a number-adding problem like this, you'll probably use a WM component called the visuospatial scratchpad, a "mind's eye" that lets you visualize the numbers, vertically arranged, long enough to do the math.

Similarly, another WM tool known as the phonological loop acts as a "mind's ear," allowing you to keep in mind the phone number you just got from directory assistance long enough to dial it. WM has its limits, as you will quickly convince yourself by trying to repeat a 12-digit number someone else has just recited. But you can learn effective strategies to improve your problem-solving skills and even sharpen your phonological loop skills.

Hormones and activation patterns may hold the answers

Not only are women better at names and dates, but recent tests have shown that women are better at WM skills as well. Again, this gender difference may lie not so much in different skill levels as in different styles of applying those skills. Brain-imaging studies have revealed different activation patterns in men's and women's brains as they solved WM puzzles.

Men showed more bilateral activity, while the women's brains were more strongly activated unilaterally. It is unclear what this says about the specific strategies they used. But whatever the strategies were, they translated into a slightly faster reaction time for men and a slightly higher accuracy rate for women.

Other research hints at why gender differences in WM brain activation patterns may exist. Frontal lobe regions underlying WM are rich with receptors for estrogen, as is the hippocampus, a brain structure used for creating and accessing long-term memories.

But no matter what strategies men and women may use solving WM puzzles, the fact remains that working memory is a faculty that is particularly vulnerable to the effects of age. Even older people who retain good memory for vocabulary and other information stored in long-term memory usually perform less well than younger people on WM tests.

There is some evidence that older women on estrogen replacement therapy are better than their untreated age-mates not only in hippocampus-dependent memory, but also on frontal lobe–dependent WM tasks. Preliminary findings also indicate that higher testosterone levels may correlate with better WM in older males. Thus the most important gender differences in memory may ultimately have to

Work Your Working Memory

Here are some fun puzzles that will give your working memory a workout. Solutions are on page 14.

What's Next?

The two tasks here activate similar skills. A is a bit easier than B because the details of a human face are more easily kept in mind than abstract patterns in B.

To solve both, your working memory must identify patterns and keep them in mind as you test them against the data. They also build powers of concentration.

A. The spring brings smiles when the sun shines and frowns when it rains. Pick one of the cartoon faces from the six in the bottom box to make the third row in the top box as complete as the top two rows. Keep an eye on those neckties!

B. The local yacht club pulled a collection of signal flags from winter storage, gave them a good wash, and hung them out to dry. Pick the signal flag from the six numbered ones on the right to complete the last row of flags on the left most logically. Par is two minutes.

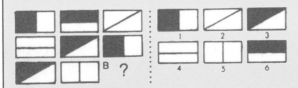

Angle-Dangle

Normally, geometric shapes are more easily visualized by male brains. In this task, though, attention to detail counts so females are also well equipped.

Kite flying is best done in springtime zephyrs, and this young man, fresh from geometry class, built his kite with triangles on his mind. How many triangles can you find in his geometric bird? Don't forget the tail. Par is five minutes.

Magic Square

A Magic Squares require patience and the ability to keep track of alternative options tried and yet to try. The math is simple; organizing strategies counts more.

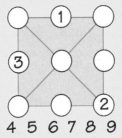

Some of the numbers have fallen out of this magic square. Can you replace the numbers in the square so that each row—horizontal, vertical or diagonal—adds up to 15?

do with how sex hormones interact differently in older men's and women's brains.

The goal of memory research, of course, is the same regardless of gender: using knowledge of the biological mechanisms of memory erosion and enhancement to keep men's and women's memories sharp throughout life.

SELF-TEST: Working Memory

This self-test is based on a neuropsychological evaluation instrument called the "n-back" test. Choose the difficulty level you want to challenge a friend to, read the instructions, and then read corresponding numbers out loud to your friend, about one per second. Your friend will have to signal you throughout the challenge—suggest lifting a finger (or some other signal that is quick, convenient and non-disruptive). At any level of difficulty, the entire series of numbers has to be completed in 30 seconds or fewer. You can also do this self-test alone, by reading through the series of numbers and circling each one that fits the requirements of whatever level of difficulty you want to try.

Note that all difficulty levels use the following number series:

2, 13, 9, 13, 7, 7, 2, 5, 12, 7, 5, 7, 8, 4, 4, 2, 3, 13, 2, 17, 4, 13, 4, 14, 5, 5, 13, 14, 9, 13

Easy WM Task
Signal whenever a number is the same as the number before it:

e.g., 13, 7, 7, 2.

Moderate WM Task
Signal whenever a number is the same as the number two numbers before it:
e.g., 7, 5, 7.

Hard WM Task
Signal whenever a number is the same as the number three numbers before it:

e.g., 13, 14, 9, 13.

Really Hard WM Task
Signal whenever a number is the same as the number four numbers before it:

e.g., 7, 2, 5, 12, 7.

Really, Really Hard WM Task
Signal whenever a number is two less than the one two numbers before it:

e.g., 9, 13, 7.

SCORING
Successful completion of any given level depends on correctly identifying the three numbers in the series that satisfy that level's instructions. At any age, anything above the Moderate Task level is more than the average person can handle.

   Allen D. Bragdon

Solution to page 13
What's Next?: A – 4; B – 6;
Angle-Dangle: We counted more than 100 triangles. The easiest way to count them is to divide the drawing into smaller symmetrical sections. Then count the number of triangles in each of the smaller sections and multiply that by the number of similar symmetrical sections. Magic Square: Row 1: 816; Row 2: 357 Row 3: 492

★ 2011 Comedy Films by John M. Samson

ACROSS

1 Slide sideways
5 Perfume from rose petals
10 Volcano near Messina
14 *Othello* antagonist
15 Blue material
16 Cross
17 2011 Jason Segel comedy
19 Astounded
20 Curaçao's chain
21 Studio supports
23 Not once, poetically
24 Debussy opus
25 Marlon in *Little Man*
28 Expatriates
31 "___ Wanna Cry": Mariah Carey
32 Chili con ___
33 Common Market: Abbr.
34 Hooligan
35 Canine woe
36 Kunis of *Black Swan*
37 Seaside bird
38 Game with 75 numbers
39 One at a sitting
40 Grapefruit divisions
42 Member of the watch
43 Broadcast sound
44 *M*A*S*H* beds
45 Kitchen dippers
47 Account
51 His, in French 101
52 2011 Kevin James comedy
54 Units of thickness
55 Lessened
56 Mist
57 Jo's sister
58 They all lead to Rome
59 Speedy jets of yore

DOWN

1 Rama's wife
2 Madeline in "Young Frankenstein"
3 "___ a Kick Out of You"
4 Like alpha males
5 Don't compare these to oranges
6 Liquor lover
7 "___ chic!"
8 Unwanted houseguest
9 Tom Arnold's ex
10 Gets the lead out
11 2011 Ben Stiller comedy
12 Christmas
13 Totals up
18 Suffix for fraud
22 Pierre's girlfriend
24 Florida key
25 Sneaky stratagems
26 Hold high
27 2011 Charlize Theron comedy
28 Forehead concealer
29 Lamprey catcher
30 Goose-pimply
32 Section of a Pound poem
35 Man of the cloth
36 Godzilla and Mothra, e.g.
38 Eliot's *Adam* ___
39 Potpourri item
41 Obstinate
42 Some billiard balls
44 Given away
45 Ewe's baby
46 "Shall Caesar send ___?": Shak.
47 Singer McEntire
48 "___ corny as Kansas ..."
49 Pass over
50 Tandoor flatbreads
53 *Boardwalk Empire* network

★★ Number Cluster

Complete the grid by constituting adjoining clusters that consist of as many cubes as the number on the cubes. At cube 5, for instance, you will have to make a five-cube cluster. Two or more figure cubes of the same value belong to the same cluster. You can only place your cubes along horizontal and/or vertical lines.

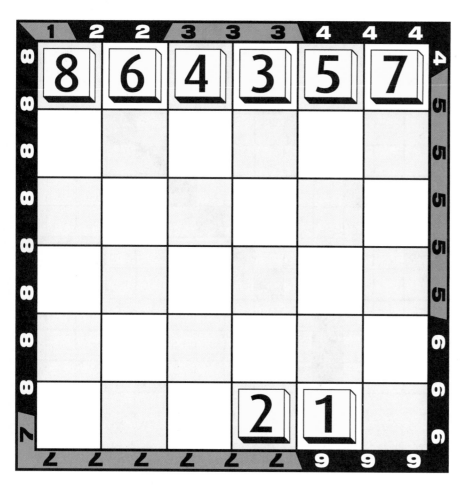

CONNECT TWO

An oxymoron is a combination of seemingly contradictory or incongruous words, such as "Science Fiction" (Science means "knowledge or study dealing with facts or truth" while Fiction means "an imagined or invented creation"). Connect the words with meanings that oppose each other and make oxymorons.

FINE   SWEAT
COLD   REALITY
RANDOM   MESS
VIRTUAL   ORDER

★ BrainSnack®—Every Second Counts

How many seconds should replace the question marks on the chronometer of rider 3?

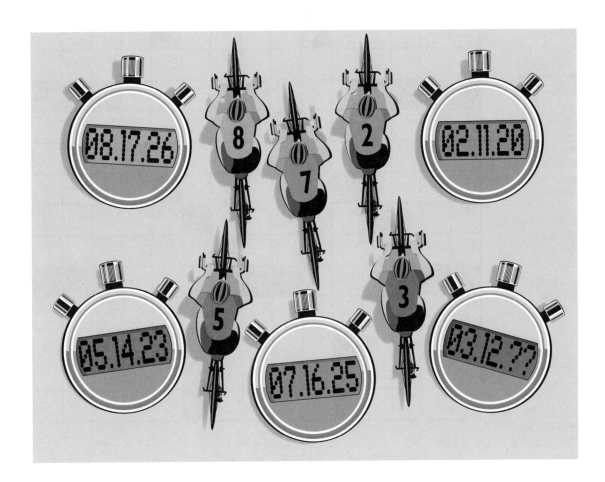

DOUBLETALK

Homophones are words that share the same pronunciation, no matter how they are spelled. If they are spelled differently then they are called heterographs. Find heterographs meaning:

PART OF A MUSICAL INSTRUMENT and AN ABILITY TO COMPREHEND WORDS AND NUMBERS

★ Geometry 101 by Karen Peterson

ACROSS

1 Cleans erasers
6 Clone
10 Arrogant one
14 Chart anew
15 Not windward
16 Double curve
17 Like a jumbuck
18 *The Lion King* lioness
19 Like anchovies
20 Coterie
23 Hydrocortisone additive
24 Back muscle
25 Shattered
28 Reside beside
33 Expressed amazement
34 Erotic
35 Upstate NY college
36 Minstrel songs
37 Stuck to
38 Foray
39 GI support group
40 Trailblazer Daniel
41 Sesame plant
42 Collegians
44 Temper
45 Brownie
46 Lotto derivative
47 Central London landmark
55 Actor's meat
56 Captive of Hercules
57 Open the toothpaste
58 Terrible czar
59 Raven's family
60 Strasbourg school
61 Await judgment
62 Pierre's head
63 Comanche shelter

DOWN

1 World's largest reptile
2 Zachary of *Less Than Perfect*
3 Mideast prince
4 IHOP stacks
5 Was in a bee
6 Hiawatha's craft
7 *Lemony Snicket* evil count
8 Lucre
9 Young thoroughbred
10 Williams in *The Big Chill*
11 Dr. Spengler in *Ghostbusters*
12 Cleave
13 Florida islets
21 Billion years
22 Cassio's adversary
25 Vet's pill
26 Standing rib
27 "Now, stop that!"
28 Adjectives modify them
29 Maritime bird
30 Trademark
31 Ponder
32 Bill attachment
34 Storyline
37 Controversy
38 Disown
40 Lugosi in *Dracula*
41 Ceremonial dinner
43 Preserve
44 ___ Plaines
46 Mardi Gras group
47 Take a header
48 Go a-wandering
49 Scottish actor Cumming
50 Clinton's veep
51 Frequently
52 *Rent-___* (Reynolds film)
53 Chest rattle
54 Thrusting sword

★ Summer

All the words are hidden vertically, horizontally or diagonally—in both directions. The letters that remain unused form a sentence from left to right.

```
I N T H E R U T S A P B E S O
U T H N E R N Y H T U E M B S
I S O O G E A P E R C H E I U
R Z E D N D I E N O L E M K N
O T I E I A S D A L A S S I S
H I G L P H H I L S D E L N H
U M O B M S M R P E E A A I I
R H D M A N U E R R H S V I N
N G O I C U U K I R Y O I I E
G W I W N S T I A E D N T C R
N S E I R R E B W A R T S E F
I M O N E U C E B R A B E C L
L T H L M S I R U O T S F R O
O O O H E A T W A V E R F E W
O O D E C E S N A T U R E A E
C I N C I P L M B I E R T M R
J A N U A R O Y T A N E D F S
S L A D N A S E B R R U A R Y
```

HEAT WAVE
HOLIDAYS
HOTEL
ICE CREAM
INSECTS
MELON
NATURE
OZONE
PASTURE
PICNIC
SALAD
SANDALS
SEASON
SOLSTICE
STRAWBERRIES
SUNSHADE
SUNSHINE
TOURISM
WATER
WIMBLEDON

AIRPLANE
BARBECUE
BIKE RIDE
BIKINI

BURN
CAMPING
COOLER
COOLING

DEHYDRATE
FESTIVALS
FLOWERS
FRUIT

MISSING LETTER MOTTO

Fill in each missing letter, indicated by an X, to make a well-known motto.

XE XREXAXEX

★★ Keep Going

Start on a blank square of your choice and connect as many blank squares as possible with one single continuous line. You can only connect squares along vertical and horizontal lines, not along diagonal lines. You must continue the connecting line up until the next obstacle, i.e., the rim of the box, a black square or a square that has already been used. You can change direction at any obstacle you meet. Each square can be used only once. The number of blank squares that will be left unused is marked in the upper square. There is more than one solution. We show only one solution.

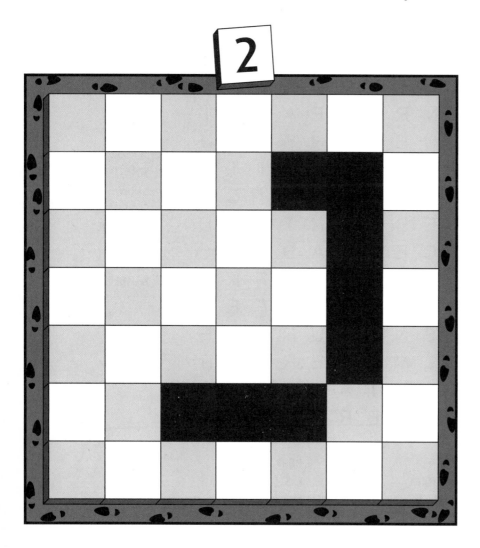

UNCANNY TURN

Rearrange the letters of the word below to form a cognate anagram, one which is related or connected in meaning to the original phrase. The answer can be one or more words.

EXACT MONIES

★ European Fare by Peggy O'Shea

ACROSS

1 Sign of freshness?
5 High-priced
10 "Love ___": Beatles
14 Story
15 Antisocial sort
16 Novello of silent films
17 Salad option
20 Saves for future use
21 Assorted
22 Beyond, in verse
23 One way to swell the ranks
24 Water bowls
28 Deviant
32 Utah ski spot
33 Retail chain link
34 Whopper
35 Brunch order
39 Her, in Hamburg
40 Conquer Kilimanjaro
41 Like a hound's nose
42 Hanna-Barbera output
44 #1 hit by the 4 Seasons
46 Blame
47 Leno or McInerney
48 Reverberant
51 Cover with water
56 Hearty fare served with croutons
58 Convex moldings
59 Give the boot
60 Excavation
61 German admiral of WWI
62 Goes out with
63 In some other manner

DOWN

1 Swirl with a spoon
2 Behind schedule
3 Sigh from Hamlet
4 Brazil soccer great
5 Works like a dog
6 Printer cartridge
7 Comes crashing down
8 Suffix for chariot
9 Opening night
10 Buster
11 Wicked
12 Kaput
13 Wild party
18 Soldering tool
19 Reddish-brown
23 Nuclear Age weapon
24 Bare-bones
25 Dog in *Up*
26 Beatle with the beat
27 Golfer Poulter
28 Molecule members
29 Change the fit
30 Saltpeter
31 Tiny
33 Climbs monkey-style
36 Serving as a symbol
37 Didn't stand tall
38 Squeak by
43 Canadian $2 coin
44 Wooden shoes
45 Song sung Sundays
47 Breakfast drink
48 Mudpuppies
49 Trim a photo
50 X, on a map
51 Cranky mood
52 Edward Cullen's adoptive mother
53 Stir things up
54 Revs the engine
55 Fencing sword
57 Spawn

★ Sudoku

Fill in the grid so that each row, each column and each 3 x 3 frame contains every number from 1 to 9.

2	5				4	6		9
			9	7	5	3		
					2		4	5
9		5		3	1	4		
7	2				6	8		
	6	4		2		9	7	
8				5	9			
					7		9	
								8

BLOCK ANAGRAM

Form the word that is described in the brackets with the letters above the grid. Extra letters are already in the right place.

CLIENT *(choice)*

★★★ Sport Maze

Draw the shortest way from the ball to the goal. You can only move along vertical and horizontal lines, not along diagonal lines. The figure on each square indicates the number of squares the ball must be moved in the same direction. You can change direction at each stop.

0	5	2	1	4	2
5	1	4	1	2	1
2	3	3	3	2	3
5	1	2	0	1	1
○	2	3	1	1	2
5	1	2	2	1	2

SANDWICH

What three-letter word belongs between the word at left and the word at right, so that the first and second word, and the second and third word, each form a common compound word or phrase?

FRONT _ _ _ LESS

★ Down Under Stars by Michele Sayer

ACROSS

1 Cook shrimp
5 Samantha in *Doctor Dolittle*
10 Bygone sovereign
14 Court proceedings
15 Zodiac sign
16 "You bet!"
17 "Nights on Broadway" singers
19 Blues legend James
20 The future
21 Also
23 *Hud* director
24 Parsonage
25 Greek metropolis
28 Went about aimlessly
31 Looks closely
32 Like knock-knock jokes
33 Where cows graze
34 "Merry Toper" painter
35 Peter in *Beat the Devil*
36 Give a ring
37 Japanese shrine city
38 Fop
39 Zellweger in *Appaloosa*
40 They know the drills
42 Various
43 Christopher in *Superman*
44 Canadian newspaper National ___
45 Against
47 Sicken
51 Give over
52 "White Shark" of golf
54 Empties (of)
55 Drew a bead on
56 Throw off, as light
57 "Paint the Sky With Stars" singer
58 Leopard markings
59 Pineapple name

DOWN

1 Quilt stuffing
2 Eight, in Madrid
3 News brief
4 Hired hands
5 Turns inside out
6 Leg of lamb
7 Husbanded
8 Lifetime
9 *SNL* character Roseannadanna
10 Botswanan fly
11 Dame Joan of opera
12 "Vissi d'___": Puccini
13 Nurture
18 Actresses Gray and Moran
22 Snowboarding stunt
24 Tie the knot
25 Insect eaten by ladybugs
26 Fluff up
27 "I Am Woman" singer
28 Things said
29 Sniggler
30 Chicago mayor in 2010
32 Adventurous tale
35 *Fear and Loathing in ___* (1998)
36 In the middle
38 Mint hardware
39 *Lethal Weapon 4* actress
41 Mother with a Nobel prize
42 Synthesizer library
44 Debra in *Love Me Tender*
45 Land measure
46 Blue cheese line
47 Disney clownfish
48 It flies through barrels
49 Comet feature
50 German duck
53 Headstone letters

★ Word Sudoku

Complete the grid so that each row, each column and each 3 x 3 frame contains the nine letters from the black box below. The hidden nine-letter word is in the diagonal from top left to bottom right.

D E F I K P Q S T

D						I		
	I		Q					
		S	I	P				F
	S	T						P
I		D	P		S	Q		
	P			Q			S	
		P	F	I				
T			I			F		
		F	E		Q	P	I	S

ONE LETTER LESS OR MORE

The word on the right side contains the letters of the word on the left side plus or minus the letter in the middle. One letter is already in the right place.

| B | A | N | D | A | G | E | S | -E | | | | B | | |

★★ BrainSnack®—Fast Lane

If you know that swimmer 9 in lane 3 will swim across the pool in 05.78 seconds and swimmer 8 in 05.97 seconds, how many seconds will swimmer 5 need?

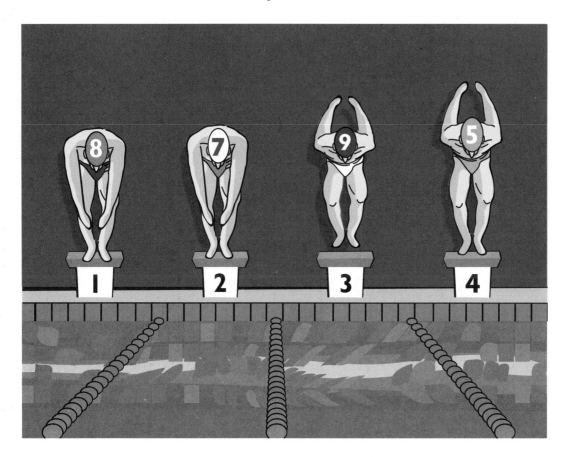

CONNECT TWO

An oxymoron is a combination of seemingly contradictory or incongruous words, such as "Science Fiction" (Science means "knowledge or study dealing with facts or truth" while Fiction means "an imagined or invented creation"). Connect the words with meanings that oppose each other and make oxymorons.

DETAILED	FOOD
SPEED	SUMMARY
FAST	PARTY
SLUMBER	LIMIT

★ Afterlife by Cindy Wheeler

ACROSS

1 Sings like Ella
6 Burial chamber
10 Religious image: Var.
14 City W of Zurich
15 Herman Melville novel
16 El ___ (ocean current)
17 *Amerika* author
18 Alicia in *Urban Legend*
19 Pixar clownfish
20 Ecstatic
23 Disney collectibles
24 Pigeon-loving Muppet
25 Iman, by birth
28 Hartley in *1969*
32 Eared seal
33 Fraternity members
34 BlackBerry maker
35 Wise man
36 Elliott in *The Shining*
37 ___ sapiens
38 Gold of *Entourage*
39 Jim Morrison's group
40 St. Andrews clod
41 David of *The X Files*
43 Detective Lupin
44 Fruit drinks
45 Urgent notation
46 Come-what-may choices
53 Wrongdoing
54 Personable
55 Mariner's *Waterworld* rescuee
56 Decor change
57 ___ even keel
58 Attention to detail
59 Forehead
60 Flat fee
61 Treat with tea

DOWN

1 H.H. Munro pen name
2 James in *Misery*
3 Cartoon barks
4 Exercise caution
5 With refinement
6 Villages
7 Fail to use
8 Puts in storage
9 Troubled
10 Congenital
11 Chicken dish
12 "This one's ___!"
13 Start of a nautical day
21 Yalie
22 Strife goddess
25 1960 Everly Brothers hit
26 Port near Sapporo
27 Hogwarts study
28 TV host Povich
29 Treasure stash
30 *The Lion King* bug eater
31 Get all histrionic
33 White lightning
36 Speed-regulating device
37 Latin-American
39 Extinct bird
40 Dresser compartments
42 Sanctify
43 Fire flakes
45 Talent peddler
46 Rosemary, e.g.
47 Eternally
48 Venetian resort
49 "Not if ___ help it"
50 For take-out
51 PayPal founder Musk
52 Like a day in June

★ Binairo

Complete the grid with zeros and ones until there are 6 zeros and 6 ones in every row and every column. No more than two of the same number can be next to or under each other. Rows or columns with exactly the same content are not allowed. There is only one valid solution.

	I			I					O		
	O				I				I		
			O	O			I				I
	O		I						I	I	
		I					I				
					O		I	I			
		I						I	I		
			O				I		I		
I			I		I		I				
								O			
I		O			O						
	O		I		O	O					

REPOSITION PREPOSITION

Unscramble I ION FUEL and find a three-word preposition.

★ Spot the Differences

Find the nine differences in the image on the right.

DELETE ONE

Delete one letter from SMART CURING UTENSILS and find a doctor's tool.

★Irate by John McCarthy

ACROSS

1 Guitar ridge
5 Amusingly odd
10 Place for a nest
14 One in a million
15 Hair-raising
16 "... ___ he said"
17 Avian mobile app game
19 One of the guys
20 Nasty
21 Calms medically
23 Allows to pass
26 Biblical verb suffix
27 More substantial
29 Bob Cratchit's boss
33 Lake Titicaca locale
34 Li'l Abner of Dogpatch
36 Transmit electronically
37 Carrey and Caviezel
38 A pain reliever
39 Ione in *River's Edge*
40 Spanish she-bear
41 *The ___ Innocence* (1993)
42 Second of two
43 Steady customer
45 China setting
47 Japanese airline
48 Pollutes
49 Frat initiations
53 Skier Lindsey
54 Rainbow goddess
55 1980 Jake La Motta biopic
60 Producer De Laurentiis
61 Tonsil neighbor
62 Nabisco cookie
63 Bob Dylan's "Gates of ___"
64 Asian palm nut
65 Be familiar with

DOWN

1 Lobster ___ Diavolo
2 Sprinted
3 Unit of work
4 Home wreckers
5 Knock down
6 Bridle
7 Captain in *Catch-22*
8 Can covers
9 ___ majesté
10 Sun-dried veggie
11 *Star Trek II: The ___* (1982)
12 Tropical vacation spot
13 Leaves
18 Himalayan mysteries
22 Skin: Comb. form
23 Mozart's *Concerto in ___*
24 Richards in *Blonde and Blonder*
25 Alfred E. Neuman is its cover boy
28 Cup of golf
29 One-man boat
30 ___-de-sac
31 Superlatively festive
32 Puts forth, as power
35 Ab ___ (from the top)
38 Turkish general
39 African antelope: Var.
41 Conservative Keyes
42 Rue Morgue murderer
44 Complete agreement
46 Like Schönberg music
49 Cloak
50 Like the Gobi
51 Lawn pest
52 Stockpile
53 Repulsive
56 Belly
57 Footed vase
58 Bloom in *The Producers*
59 Holstein hello

★ Cage the Animals

Draw lines to completely divide up the grid into small squares with exactly one animal per square. The squares should not overlap.

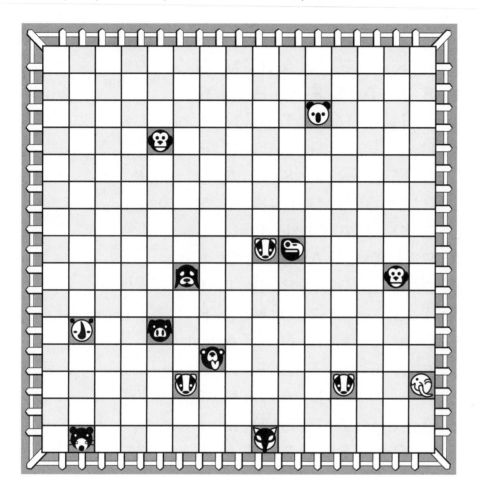

DOUBLETALK

Homophones are words that share the same pronunciation, no matter how they are spelled. If they are spelled differently then they are called heterographs. Find heterographs meaning:

A UNIT OF TIME and BELONGING TO US

★ Tolkien

All the words are hidden vertically, horizontally or diagonally—in both directions. The letters that remain unused form a sentence from left to right.

```
I S G T S R E D I P S T O O S
K T R O A O L K I E N A L M G
C L O O L Y S E T T E N H Y N
E A E B O L L O R T T A R I
L T B S I T U I F I E L D S R
E R T I T L S M V R A S O W R
B O I A F T B E D G D N H I S
R M B S V U O O S A R I L U L
I M E L D A R I O N A L M O L
M I R K W O O D L D V B D I I
B N O O U N T S A A A O N S H
O D D U I E U M H L R G Y A N
R M N R M S L W T F T E R R O
I O O U S B K V I I M A O U R
S H G R T E A R E Z B G P M I
T I E C D E S R L S A B O A R
J A C K S O N D O R F R O N T
H E R I G O R L A B N G D H S
```

FRODO
GANDALF
GOBLINS
GOLLUM
GONDOR
HOBBIT
IMMORTAL
IRON HILLS
JACKSON
MIRKWOOD
MORDOR
ORODRETH
RINGS
SARUMAN
SPIDERS
STOORS
THALOS
THORIN
TROLL
TULKAS
UMBAR
VARDA
VILYA
WIZARD

ARAGORN
BALROG
BATTLE

BIFUR
BILBO
CELEBRIMBOR

ELDARION
ELVES
FIELDS

CHANGE ONE

Change one letter in each of these two words to form a common two-word phrase. There may be more than one possible answer.

HOME TACK

★★ Sunny Weather

Where will the sun shine? With the knowledge that each arrow points to a place where a symbol should be, can you locate the sunny spots? The symbols cannot be next to each other vertically, horizontally or diagonally. A symbol cannot be placed on top of an arrow. We show one symbol.

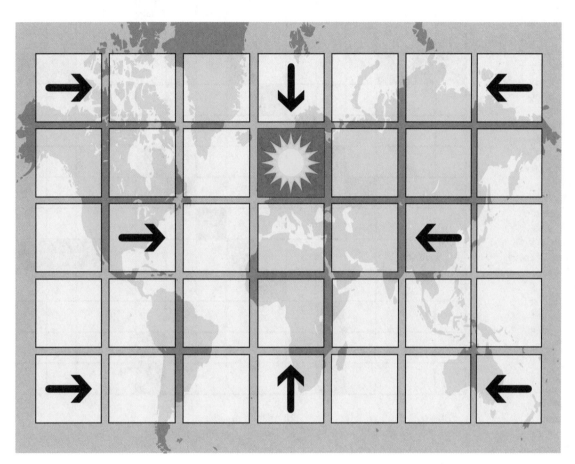

SANDWICH

What four-letter word belongs between the word at left and the word at right, so that the first and second word, and the second and third word, each form a common compound word or phrase?

MASTER _ _ _ _ BLOWER

★ Oh Oh! by Maggie Ellis

ACROSS
1 Winglike
5 Zaharias and Ruth
10 Shout on deck
14 Rhythmic speed
15 Uplift
16 Partner of bother
17 Underhanded change
19 Get outta town
20 Permanent
21 *The Naked and the Dead* author
23 Half-pint
24 Native Israeli
25 Began to develop
28 Pickled veggie
31 *On Golden Pond* heroine
32 Had better
33 Firehouse tool
34 Mental state
35 Teasdale and Allgood
36 Lena in *Casanova*
37 Game based on crazy eights
38 Tow truck in *Cars*
39 Tight-lipped
40 Working again
42 Road Runner's foe
43 "No mas" boxer Roberto
44 Soothing lotion
45 Folklore fairy king
47 Continental
51 Dummkopf
52 Australian instrument
54 Way out
55 *Swan Lake* villainess
56 Supermarket lineup
57 Athenian portico
58 Compound in fireworks
59 Captain Hook's underling

DOWN
1 Vaulted cathedral area
2 Tennis type
3 Sulfuric ___
4 Came full circle
5 Trailing
6 Ain't put right?
7 Floating ice mass
8 Habitat: Comb. form
9 Food processors?
10 Declare to be true
11 Loud clamor
12 Hosea, in the Douay Bible
13 River into North Sea
18 Inhumane
22 Lean against
24 Cane product
25 Show reluctance
26 Make amends
27 "Hallelujah!"
28 Like Virginia hams
29 Occupy time and space
30 Zellweger in *Nurse Betty*
32 Like some hay
35 Susan in *Alfie*
36 2012 London event
38 Spanish surrealist
39 Crayola choice
41 Dawn deity
42 Chosen pursuit
44 Taps sounder
45 Line at the track
46 Jodhpur, e.g.
47 Review a review, say
48 Netherlands cheese
49 Front-rank
50 Pinocchio's lie detector
53 "Big Daddy" Amin

★ Kakuro

Each number in a black area is the sum of the numbers that you have to enter in the next empty boxes. The empty boxes that make up the sum are called a run. The sum of the across run is written above the diagonal in the black area and the sum of the down run is written below the diagonal. Runs can only contain the numbers 1 through 9 and each number in a run can only be used once. The gray boxes only contain odd numbers and the white only even numbers.

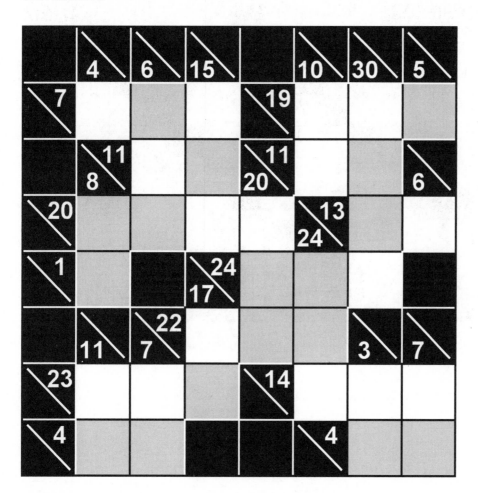

LETTERBLOCKS

Move the letterblocks around so that words are formed on top and below that you can associate with professions.

★★ BrainSnack®—Slots

Which wheel (1–5) on this gambling machine is not identical to the strip underneath?

LETTER LINE

Put a letter in each of the squares below to make a word which means "ONE WHO DOESN'T PAY." These numbered clues refer to other words which can be made from the whole.

6 2 8 3 7 5 BAD EXPERIENCE; 2 3 7 8 9 2
A BOOK OF WRITINGS; 1 3 8 9 2 7 5 SYSTEM OF GOVERNMENT;
8 3 7 5 3 2 ONE WHO HOLDS THE CARDS

1	2	3	4	5	6	7	8	9	10

★ Cities of the World by Cindy Wheeler

ACROSS

1 Babylon's land
5 Stomach woe
10 Leave hastily
14 *Enterprise* helmsman
15 Hourly
16 *Rubáiyát* rhyme scheme
17 Ethiopia's largest city
19 On who exploits
20 Knee jerk, e.g.
21 Locust
23 Canterbury's shire
24 *The Alienist* author Carr
25 Cover girls, e.g.
28 Belgian battle site of 1815
31 Mistreat
32 Renowned
33 Total up
34 Bird's-___ soup
35 Was concerned
36 Koko's weapon
37 CIA precursor
38 Trendy mushroom
39 Rio Grande feeder
40 1975 Morris Albert hit single
42 Snack for a monkey
43 Slowly, to Solti
44 *Jesu, Joy of ___ Desiring*: Bach
45 Calm down
47 To this matter, in legalese
51 Novello of *The White Rose*
52 Gateway Arch city
54 Graceful aquatic bird
55 Wound-up
56 Maui music makers
57 Barks in comic strips
58 Bangladesh instrument
59 Snakebite cures

DOWN

1 Munich river
2 Brusque
3 *M*A*S*H* star
4 Superlatively speedy
5 Jacob Marley's burden
6 Steel-collar worker
7 Islands near Galway Bay
8 Mercutio's subject
9 Gained the good will of
10 Teacup holder
11 Morocco's largest city
12 Sacked out
13 *Gone With the Wind* manor
18 Carved stone marker
22 "Where Is the Life That Late ___?"
24 Llama relative
25 ___ *La Mancha* (1972)
26 Way past plump
27 Cologne's rival city
28 Inventory items
29 Concert hall
30 Ukrainian port, to natives
32 North Dakota's largest city
35 Objects to the will
36 Like exotic dancing
38 Breath freshener
39 *American Idol* group
41 Finds out
42 Cashless deal
44 High-IQ org.
45 ___spell (relax)
46 At all times
47 Clue
48 Microwave
49 Stadium level
50 Mountain in Thessaly
53 Start of a vowel sequence

★★ Keep Going

Start on a blank square of your choice and connect as many blank squares as possible with one single continuous line. You can only connect squares along vertical and horizontal lines, not along diagonal lines. You must continue the connecting line up until the next obstacle, i.e., the rim of the box, a black square or a square that has already been used. You can change direction at any obstacle you meet. Each square can be used only once. The number of blank squares that will be left unused is marked in the upper square. There is more than one solution. We show only one solution.

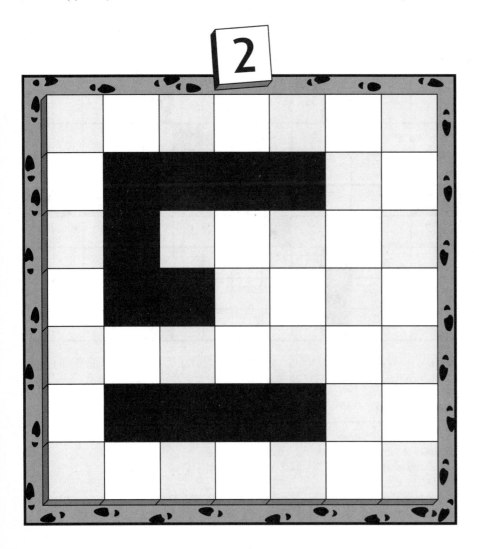

UNCANNY TURN

Rearrange the letters of the word below to form a cognate anagram, one which is related or connected in meaning to the original phrase. The answer can be one or more words.

SIT CHAT PAY SIR

★★ Sudoku

Fill in the grid so that each row, each column and each 3 x 3 frame contains every number from 1 to 9.

2	8						7	
				7	3			8
		4			1			
			3	4	5	9		7
7	5		9		8		3	
6	2		4	5	9			
4	1	7						
8							6	3

CONNECT TWO

An oxymoron is a combination of seemingly contradictory or incongruous words, such as "Science Fiction" (Science means "knowledge or study dealing with facts or truth" while Fiction means "an imagined or invented creation"). Connect the words with meanings that oppose each other and make oxymorons.

ACTIVE   MARKET
ACCURATE   GRIEF
FREE   RETIREMENT
GOOD   ESTIMATE

★ Seasonal by Cindy Wheeler

ACROSS

1 Apple computer
5 Holy Ark scrolls
10 First bone donor
14 Noted flood survivor
15 Down East college town
16 Carolina rail
17 Small gazelles
19 Saucy sort
20 Lea lows
21 Gains altitude
23 Spiner in *Star Trek Nemesis*
26 Hellenic H
27 Turn in for money
29 Underscored
34 Skittish
35 Adulates
37 Sun-dance tribe
38 Botanist Gray et al.
39 Big star, briefly
40 Mrs. David Bowie
41 Thrice: Rx
42 Conjure up
43 Livy's 2,002
44 Mayflower
46 Places for awareness ribbons
48 Wrath
49 By itself
50 Fund-raising event
54 Russian river
56 Pilaster
57 Lee Majors series
62 Russian turndown
63 Use as a dining table
64 Cape Breton Island language
65 Golfer Nicklaus
66 Thick
67 "Endless Love" is one

DOWN

1 Ones with clout
2 Messy do
3 Berne river
4 Christmas Eve entryways
5 Words in a takeout order
6 Spheres
7 Kanga's kid
8 "My Way" composer
9 "Big" star on *Pawn Stars*
10 Annual report listing
11 "Hot Stuff" singer
12 Like the Karakum
13 Navigator's stack
18 Steno's reminder
22 Bee followers
23 Something drawn
24 Parted waters in Exodus
25 "Frankenstein" group
28 Keystroke sequence
29 Large seabird
30 Waste allowance
31 Convention flouter
32 Sells online
33 Fitness expert Austin
36 Animal in the song "Do-Re-Mi"
40 Driven
42 Gordon Ramsay, notably
45 War ender
47 "Be ___ and help me out here!"
50 Explosive sound
51 One-named Irish singer
52 Object
53 Spicy Asian cuisine
54 Sky mysteries
55 Philippic
58 Abbr. at LAX
59 *Despicable Me* villain
60 "___ your head!"
61 However

★ Futoshiki

Fill in the 5 x 5 grid with the numbers from 1 to 5 once per row and column, while following the greater than/lesser than symbols shown. There is only one valid solution that can be reached through logic and clear thinking alone!

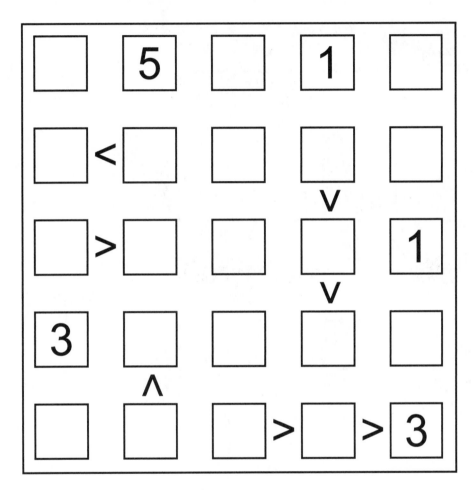

ONE LETTER LESS OR MORE

The word on the right side contains the letters of the word on the left side plus or minus the letter in the middle. One letter is already in the right place.

D E C I M A L S -S- M ☐ ☐ ☐ ☐ ☐ ☐

★ Word Sudoku

Complete the grid so that each row, each column and each 3 x 3 frame contains
the nine letters from the black box below. The hidden nine-letter word is in the
diagonal from top left to bottom right.

A E G I L O S T X

BLOCK ANAGRAM

Form the word that is described in the brackets with the letters above the grid. Extra letters are
already in the right place.

ART DECO (popular)

| | | M | | C | | | I | |

★★★ BrainSnack®—Foul Play

The referee has signaled a foul where a soccer ball is located. In which square (1–12) will a player commit the next foul knowing that the field is divided into square zones?

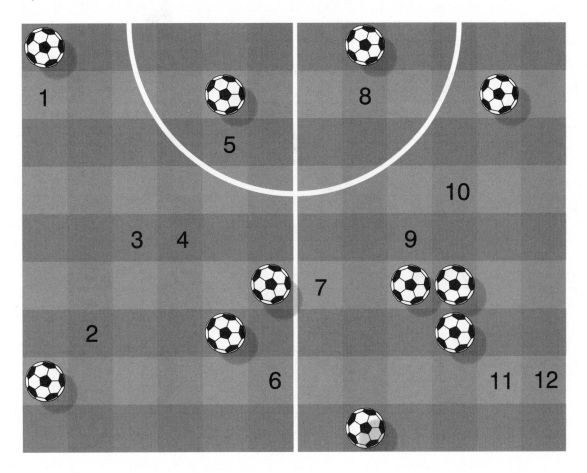

SANDWICH

What four-letter word belongs between the word at left and the word at right, so that the first and second word, and the second and third word, each form a common compound word or phrase?

B O O K _ _ _ _ D O W N

★ Holiday Songs by Peggy O'Shea

ACROSS

1 Eastern nursemaid
5 De la Garza of *Law & Order*
10 Get teary
14 Petty in *Free Willy*
15 Chest
16 Jazz great Hines
17 "White Christmas" singer
19 Folk singer Guthrie
20 Tavern
21 Seasoned
23 2001 Uma Thurman film
24 Will in *Ali*
25 Goal
28 *Gilligan's Island* star
31 Campus newbie
32 Father's Day gift
33 Mitchell in *Honeydripper*
34 It may be shaken in anger
35 Ill-chosen
36 ___ julep
37 Old English letter
38 Doozies
39 Altercation
40 Considered
42 Dolly in *Steel Magnolias*
43 Straightedge
44 Voting group
45 "For richer, for ___ ..."
47 Dark-haired
51 Timber wolf
52 "Don't Save It All for Christmas Day" singer
54 Ending for cell
55 Putting to a purpose
56 Sailor's saint
57 Capital of Yemen
58 Wigwam cousin
59 Legion

DOWN

1 *Fantastic Four* star Jessica
2 Drudgery
3 "Rule, Britannia!" composer
4 Top grade of gasoline
5 Steeply inclined
6 Unrestrained
7 South African fox
8 San Francisco hill
9 *Crank* star
10 Affluence
11 "Santa Baby" singer
12 ___ Stanley Gardner
13 Move slowly
18 Jim Boeheim, for one
22 "___ She Sweet?"
24 Falls off
25 House bid
26 Maid of honor's concern

27 *Noël* is his Christmas album
28 "___ Rain's A-Gonna Fall": Dylan
29 How dirges are played
30 "Rocket Man" singer John
32 Make plain one's disdain
35 Sell for less
36 German car
38 Heraldic border
39 River of Lyon
41 Disney's *Sleeping Beauty* princess
42 Fall precipitously
44 Pickle juice
45 Math sign
46 Jabba the Hutt's dancer
47 Radar bogey

48 Register
49 Library book
50 Sufficient, in verse
53 "-ish" alternative

★ Cage the Animals

Draw lines to completely divide up the grid into small squares with exactly one animal per square. The squares should not overlap.

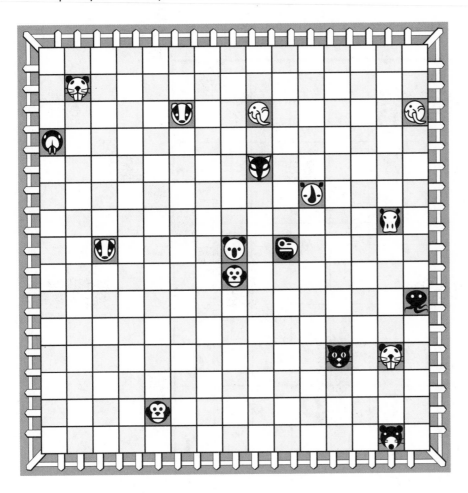

★ Binairo

Complete the grid with zeros and ones until there are 5 zeros and 6 ones in every row and every column. No more than two of the same number can be next to or under each other. Rows or columns with exactly the same content are not allowed. There is only one valid solution.

		1			1					
				0		1				
		1				1		1		
	1		1	1						1
									0	1
0		1				1		1		
		1		1						0
				0		0				
1	0		0			1				0
1			1		0				1	0

DOUBLETALK

Homophones are words that share the same pronunciation, no matter how they are spelled. If they are spelled differently then they are called heterographs. Find heterographs meaning:

A STREAM and A SOUND

★★ Antagonists by Don Law

ACROSS

1 Squire-to-be
5 Inch along
10 Like sharp cheese
14 Alpine goat
15 Big Three conference site
16 Repetitive process
17 *Titanic* antagonist
19 Cudgel
20 Stares at
21 Charging need
23 Blackened, Cajun-style
26 Military uniform material
27 Went postal
28 Emeril, for one
29 Well-used pencil
32 Laura of *ER*
33 Stiff-backed
34 Main mailbox locale: Abbr.
35 Scary stop
36 ___ havoc on
37 *I, Claudius* emperor
38 "Trivial Pursuit" piece
39 Leigh in *Psycho*
40 Ono and Watanabe
41 Bow wood
42 Geraint's consort
43 Eat like a bird
44 Pointless
46 Men of Portugal
47 Silvery lead ore
49 Way to a man's heart
50 Signs on the dotted line
51 *Back to the Future* antagonist
56 Leave in, to a proofreader
57 Yahoo! service
58 Bedrock abode
59 Dick Tracy's Trueheart
60 Waterfall effect
61 Sword with a bell

DOWN

1 Photo
2 Attorney's org.
3 Hair stuff
4 Urged strongly
5 Biked
6 Made a leaf pile
7 Plumbing connections
8 Warm days in Cannes
9 2003 Ben Affleck film
10 *As You Like It* forest
11 *Wall Street* antagonist
12 Needle case
13 Unpaid balance
18 Fairy-tale heavies
22 Falling-out
23 Like Peking duck
24 Tearjerker need
25 *Misery* antagonist
26 Not play fair
28 Apollo in *Rocky*

30 Hullabaloo
31 Gives a lift to
33 Davis of *The Express*
36 Emulators
37 "When hell freezes over!"
39 *The Prime of Miss ___ Brodie* (1969)
40 Yiddish busybody
43 With impudence
45 Tree homes
46 Capital of Bulgaria
47 Main idea
48 Poker stake
49 Off in the distance
52 Holy terror
53 Drift off
54 Robot in *WALL-E*
55 By birth

★ BrainSnack®—Spot the Lily

Which water lily (1–6) doesn't belong to the same family as all the others?

MISSING LETTER MOTTO

Fill in each missing letter, indicated by an X, to make a well-known motto.

XO XRXTECX AXX TX XERXE

★ Rivers

All the words are hidden vertically, horizontally or diagonally—in both directions. The letters that remain unused form a sentence from left to right.

```
G A N G E S N T A M A Z O N H
C E L E N O A G L O V C F T B
A O E N K A K A N D E E R I G
I H L U T I B E R N N J T B A
P E Y O P A N U I K G A E O F
P B E A R H G H K R O N D I D
I L V R E A R U R A D U N M A
S E C S P N D A S R R D A A N
S E O I R S E O T E O D R R U
I N N R E N E C V E D T G N B
S O G G S E M I K R S M O E E
S S O I E I R I N A E D I F R
I D A T W D O G S M R T R S S
M U O N E G A N H S E V E I E
E H W R P I S O N Z O V O I M
O R I N O C O K N T E U O F A
R I O D U L C E T R H E R S H
O N A D R O J M N U R C E I T
```

MEKONG
MISSISSIPPI
MISSOURI
NECKAR
ONEGA
ORINOCO
RED RIVER
RHINE
RIO DULCE
RIO GRANDE
SEVERN
SPREE
TAGUS
THAMES
TIBER
TIGRIS
VOLGA
WESER
YUKON

AISNE
AMAZON
COLORADO
CONGO
DANUBE
DORDOGNE
DUNAJEC
ELBE
EUPHRATES
GANGES
HUDSON
ISONZO
JORDAN
KUBAN
MARNE

DELETE ONE

Delete one letter from RIDICULOUS and find another just as outrageous.

★★ Britannia by John M. Samson

ACROSS

1 Pop singer Anthony
5 Milkshake stick-in
10 Movie composer Zimmer
14 Fragrance
15 Conductor Kunzel
16 In a rank
17 Peace Nobelist Eisaku
18 Al Capone's "Enforcer"
19 Prefix for legal
20 Euphemism for *Macbeth*
23 Feeling it, so to speak
24 Summer shirt
25 Tomei in *The Ides of March*
28 Newfoundland time
33 Catkin
34 Wing-footed
35 Screen star Lupino
36 Helgenberger of *CSI*
37 Moray hunter
38 Waste allowance
39 A/C measure
40 Comedian Cohen
41 Hornswoggle
42 Salve
44 Like formalwear
45 Witchy month: Abbr.
46 Lend an ear
47 Diana's title
55 Macnee's *The Avengers* co-star
56 Class-A
57 *La Dolce* ___ (1960)
58 Baseball brothers
59 Skin conditioner
60 Panache
61 "A ___ pittance!"
62 Evening shoes
63 Snoot

DOWN

1 Over fifty percent
2 Esau's wife
3 One way to learn
4 Intersection
5 Spanish lady
6 Hackneyed
7 *Norma Rae* director
8 West End opener
9 He painted his mother
10 Come about
11 Kazakhstan sea
12 *Julie & Julia* director Ephron
13 Move in the breeze
21 Expenditure
22 Qualifying race
25 Caribbean dance
26 Big name in violins
27 Lucy's brother in *Peanuts*
28 Give out shares
29 Preadult
30 Michelins, e.g.
31 Concepts
32 Subtly malicious
34 Potted plant
37 Canines that bite
38 Classic Poe poem
40 Roman 2,200
41 Bird's crop
43 Bell clapper
44 Puts off
46 Encore Las Vegas, for one
47 Hyde Park carriage
48 Get one's blood boiling
49 Borodin's *Prince* ___
50 Fruit similar to a plum
51 Trigonometry curve
52 ___ *and Stitch* (2002)
53 Greek vowels
54 All there

★★★ BrainSnack®—Name It

Which letter should replace the question mark on the last card?

CONNECT TWO

An oxymoron is a combination of seemingly contradictory or incongruous words, such as "Science Fiction" (Science means "knowledge or study dealing with facts or truth" while Fiction means "an imagined or invented creation"). Connect the words with meanings that oppose each other and make oxymorons.

ALMOST	MAN
LADIES	GAS
LIQUID	BATH
MUD	EXACTLY

★★ Sudoku

Fill in the grid so that each row, each column and each 3 x 3 frame contains every number from 1 to 9.

6			2		7	3		5
	2		3		9			
7		3	4		5			
9	3		1			8		
	7	5		4		6		2
		6	9				5	
				3		5		1
4						7		
				8				

UNCANNY TURN

Rearrange the letters of the word below to form a cognate anagram, one which is related or connected in meaning to the original phrase. The answer can be one or more words.

SO TRUSTY MEN JOKE AND WIN PRAISE

★★ Give and Take by Linda Lather

ACROSS
1 St. Louis team
5 Family tree branches
10 "Auld ___ Syne"
14 Figure skater Kulik
15 Far from cheap
16 *House of Wax* henchman
17 "You go, ___!"
18 Taunt
19 Fernandez of tennis
20 Expires
23 Grab a chair
24 Tent bunk
25 Go hurriedly
29 Chide
33 Rowling's Madam Pince et al.
34 Swamp bird
36 Tic-tac-toe line
37 "My Heart Will ___": Dion
38 Great Dane bane
39 Extinct German ox
40 Mount where Aaron died
41 Schooner power
42 *The Maltese Falcon* sleuth
43 One demanding proof
45 Prices for clearance
47 Devour
48 NYC time zone
49 Rise above it all
58 "Fourth Stooge" Sitka
59 Flower goddess
60 Hard to handle
61 "Peter Pan" pirate
62 WWII vessel
63 Square column
64 Snitched
65 Minor error
66 Armstrong walked on it

DOWN
1 Diana of *The Avengers*
2 Part of et al.
3 ICBM warhead
4 Miller's *Death of a ___*
5 Savvy
6 El Paso college
7 Uncluttered
8 "Winter Song" pianist John
9 Toastmaster talks
10 Times Square sights
11 Exchange premium
12 Beaten-egg beverages
13 Guts
21 Enjoys brandy
22 Fall guy
25 Venice's Bridge of ___
26 Scam artist
27 Love, Italian style
28 Museum showpiece
29 Boorish
30 Bar mitzvah reading
31 Ooze
32 Sniffers
35 Toothpaste type
38 Stephen King baseball book
39 How salmon swim
41 RN's "at once!"
42 Miss Universe wear
44 Removed the rind
46 Papal emissary
49 Trial run
50 Bullets
51 German canal city
52 Napoleon's isle of exile
53 Hula-___
54 Pension plans
55 Wine combiner
56 Chorale member
57 Cannon in *Heaven Can Wait*

★ Word Sudoku

Complete the grid so that each row, each column and each 3 x 3 frame contains the nine letters from the black box below. The hidden nine-letter-word is in the diagonal from top left to bottom right.

D E F G I N R V Y

V	G			Y	R			
	E		G	N	D	V		
	R			I				N
F	R	V	I	D		G	Y	
E				V	N	I		
I					F			
	V	E		R				Y
R			D					F

SANDWICH

What four-letter word belongs between the word at left and the word at right, so that the first and second word, and the second and third word, each form a common compound word or phrase?

B E L T _ _ _ _ A G E

★★★ Sport Maze

Draw the shortest way from the ball to the goal. You can only move along vertical and horizontal lines, not along diagonal lines. The figure on each square indicates the number of squares the ball must be moved in the same direction. You can change direction at each stop.

3	2	1	4	1	2
3	2	4	1	2	2
2	2	2	1	4	
3	2	2	3	1	5
3	4	4	2	2	5
3	1	5	1	5	0

REPOSITION PREPOSITION

Unscramble OF NO POT and find a three-word preposition.

★★ Golden Globe Nominees by Michele Sayer

ACROSS

1 Small weight
5 Pancho's pal
10 Santa's burden
14 Racing sled
15 Written in a specified key
16 Kyrgyzstan range
17 Utilizer
18 Chewy candy
19 *Ocean's Twelve* heroine
20 2011 Ryan Gosling film
23 Thieves' retreat
24 "Harper Valley ___" (1968 hit)
25 Waltzer of song
29 Touchdown site
33 Film director Kazan
34 Mount climbed by Moses
36 Think better of
37 2011 Woody Allen film
41 "I Was the ___": Presley
42 Fertile soil
43 A real money maker
44 Term
46 Attaché's milieu
49 Isn't anymore
50 Bireme puller
51 2011 George Clooney film
59 What Yale became in 1969
60 Sneak off to marry
61 Japanese shrine center
62 Sweat outlet
63 Like hot fudge
64 Streetcar
65 In good time
66 Twins share them
67 Talk up

DOWN

1 Surplus
2 Charge the quarterback
3 Awry, in London
4 Prime ___
5 Be present at
6 Extinct birds of New Zealand
7 Skinny
8 Hook for landing fish
9 Michael Phelps, notably
10 Petty dictator
11 "Smart" guy
12 Funds
13 Grafton's ___ *for Killer*
21 Costa ___ Sol
22 Off the bottom, as an anchor
25 In-box stack
26 Classic dress style
27 *The Prince of ___* (1991)
28 Pasty
29 Licorice plant
30 Gold braid
31 The Acropolis, e.g.
32 Surly
35 "___ a boy!"
38 Trojan War epic
39 Score of zero
40 Imaginary undying flower
45 Annika Sorenstam's homeland
47 "___ no object!"
48 Good, in street talk
51 Betty Boop, e.g.
52 Knight in shining armor
53 Wild plum
54 Crockett's hat source
55 Sword with a button
56 Not even one
57 Mouse catcher
58 Identical
59 Tax-return pro

★★ BrainSnack®—How Cheesy!

Which flag (1–6) belongs on the last cheese cube?

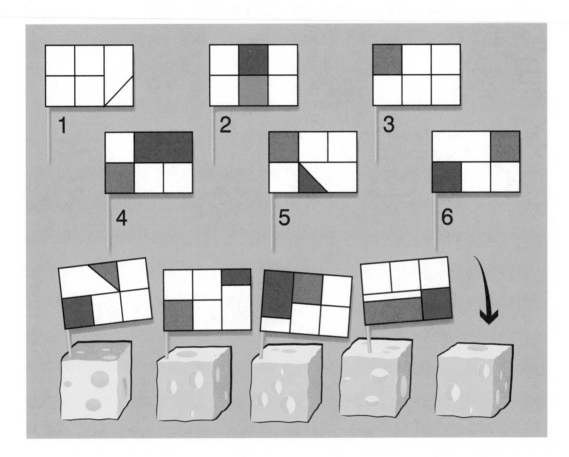

LETTERBLOCKS

Move the letterblocks around so that words are formed on top and below that you can associate with insects.

★ Sudoku Twin

Fill in the grid so that each row, each column and each 3 x 3 frame contains every number from 1 to 9. A sudoku twin is two connected 9 x 9 sudokus.

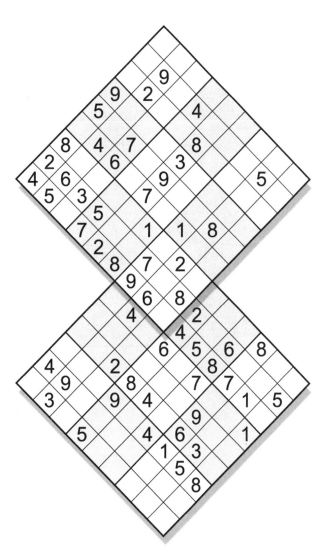

CHANGE ONE

Change one letter in each of these two words to form a common two-word phrase. There may be more than one possible answer.

FLOP RIDE

★★ Pretty Cheesy by Karen Peterson

ACROSS

1 Fishnet stocking material
5 Applauds
10 Sea-green
14 Sarah McLachlan hit
15 Alex Jones medium
16 Warbled
17 Rustic lodgings
18 Nuclear weapon
19 Grant by treaty
20 Cheesy pasta dish
22 Melodic opera passages
24 Ross Ice ___
26 Scintilla
27 Coffee orders
30 Wilson in *Midnight in Paris*
32 Form a hollow
35 "What ___!" ("Hilarious!")
36 Piqued states
37 Nuptial pledge
38 Blowgun ammo
39 Righteous
40 Jane Lynch series
41 Suffix for tank
42 Holler
43 Green energy
44 Shanghai's Jin ___ Tower
45 Hors d'oeuvre item
46 Sand bars
47 Round bread of India
49 Mouth-watering
51 ___ for Humanity
54 Cheesy Italian pastry
58 Hole punching tools
59 Midwest tribe
61 Zeal
62 Josh Groban Christmas album
63 ___ and a leg
64 Site for soap
65 Stickum
66 Says no to
67 Irish ___ bread

DOWN

1 Crusader's wear
2 Tracy's *Hairspray* mom
3 Seven deadly ___
4 Isn't out of the running
5 Whooping birds
6 Not generic
7 Trivial fuss
8 Egyptian cotton
9 Temperance
10 Sporty scarf
11 Cheesy Mexican snack
12 Reverse
13 Broadway's *Rock of ___*
21 Steps to the Ganges
23 Positive ray particles
25 Cheesy Swiss dishes
27 Lady of the house

28 Scarlett of Tara
29 Cheesy chicken dish
31 Hoops great Chamberlain
33 Quintessential
34 Busy bodies?
36 Chimney blackener
39 Accra resident
40 "My word!"
42 Baby oyster
43 Tibia
46 Cramps, e.g.
48 Path through seats
50 Without ___ in the world
51 Dangle
52 Wayward GI
53 *Beloved* novelist Morrison
55 Melange

56 Touch down
57 Durante's "___ Dinka Doo"
60 Cheese covering

★★ Sunny Weather

Where will the sun shine? With the knowledge that each arrow points to a place where a symbol should be, can you locate the sunny spots? The symbols cannot be next to each other vertically, horizontally or diagonally. A symbol cannot be placed on top of an arrow. We show one symbol.

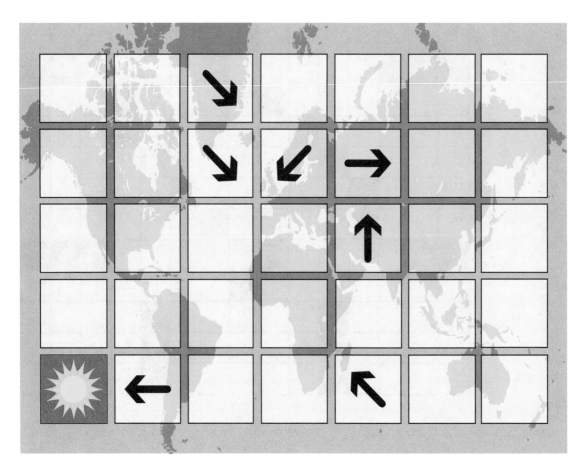

CONNECT TWO

An oxymoron is a combination of seemingly contradictory or incongruous words, such as "Science Fiction" (Science means "knowledge or study dealing with facts or truth" while Fiction means "an imagined or invented creation"). Connect the words with meanings that oppose each other and make oxymorons.

MINOR	DIVORCE
NEVER	DONATION
REQUIRED	MIRACLE
AMICABLE	AGAIN

★★★ BrainSnack®—Flag It!

Which digits are missing on the flag with question marks?

DOUBLETALK

Homophones are words that share the same pronunciation, no matter how they are spelled. If they are spelled differently then they are called heterographs. Find heterographs meaning:

SITUATED IN FRONT and A NUMBER

★ Safe Code

To open the safe you have to replace the question mark with the correct figure. You can find this figure by determining the logical method behind the numbers shown. The method may include calculation, inversion, repetition, chronological succession, or forming ascending and descending series.

SAFE A08

BLOCK ANAGRAM

Form the word that is described in the brackets with the letters above the grid. Extra letters are already in the right place.

A PENCIL (in opposition to a monarchy)

R | | | U | B | | | | | |

★★ Themeless by Don Law

ACROSS
1 Without control
5 Police entrapment
10 Chi followers
14 Rafa Nadal's uncle/ coach
15 Cartoon Viking
16 Interlaken river
17 Divisible by two
18 Frugal
20 Close one
22 X out
23 Sewing line
24 Eric the Red's century
25 Nose partitions
28 As above
32 Fielding flubs
34 Motel room
35 Cytoplasm component
36 High time
37 Short and direct
39 Short skirt
40 "___ bodkins!"
41 "Love ___": Beatles
42 Spectacles
44 Tebow targets
47 Apprehensive
48 Bury
49 "___ Old Black Magic"
51 Drove a rig
53 Pledged
57 Misanthropic
59 Former Japanese capital
60 Tent beds
61 Hasty
62 Boyish smile
63 Sheepshank, for one
64 Heavenly places
65 Santa's bag

DOWN
1 Solar disk
2 Turn to play
3 "The ___ Love": R.E.M.
4 Jamaican capital
5 Ancient queendom
6 Toyota pickup
7 Aircraft designer Sikorsky
8 Publisher Talese
9 Shopping list staples
10 Dabbles in oils
11 Mawkish
12 *Dies* ___
13 Order to the broker
19 Zola portraitist
21 Get the word
24 Large quantities
25 Casa mister
26 Undercut
27 Italian ham
29 Commotion
30 More private
31 *The Great Gatsby* heroine
33 Dockworker
38 River of central Germany
39 Get-togethers
41 Chiggers
43 Hardly a chatterbox
45 Join the service
46 Use a colander
50 Wrestler's arsenal
51 Potboiler writer
52 By and by
53 Meerschaum
54 Poet Teasdale
55 Bana of *Hulk*
56 Disagreeably damp
58 Stinker

★ Hourglass

Starting in the middle, each word in the top half has the letters of the word below it, plus a new letter, and each word in the bottom half has the letters of the word above it, plus a new letter.

(1) tries
(2) sacred songs
(3) muscular contraction
(4) a large number of
(5) military dining room
(6) appears
(7) tropical herb
(8) content

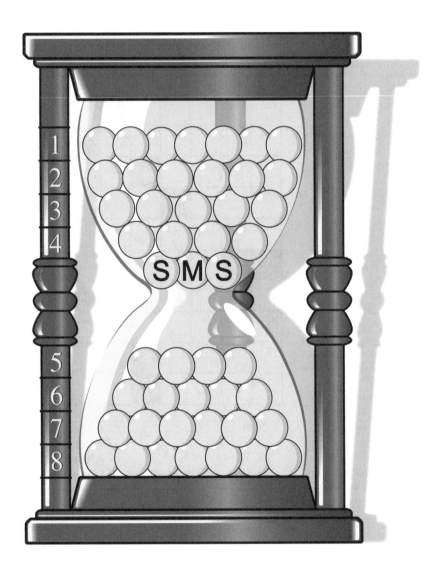

SANDWICH

What five-letter word belongs between the word at left and the word at right, so that the first and second word, and the second and third word, each form a common compound word or phrase?

LIGHTNING _ _ _ _ _ BACK

★★ Keep Going

Start on a blank square of your choice and connect as many blank squares as possible with one single continuous line. You can only connect squares along vertical and horizontal lines, not along diagonal lines. You must continue the connecting line up until the next obstacle, i.e., the rim of the box, a black square or a square that has already been used. You can change direction at any obstacle you meet. Each square can be used only once. The number of blank squares that will be left unused is marked in the upper square. There is more than one solution. We show only one solution.

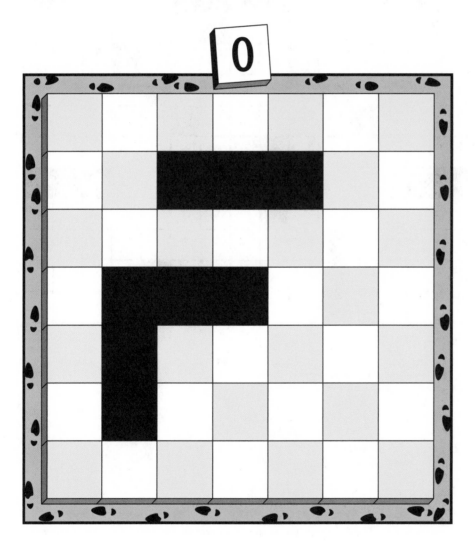

DELETE ONE

Delete one letter from HAS TO PILFER and find the culprit.

★★ Repeat Openers by Maggie Ellis

ACROSS

1 Polynesian dance
5 Bearer of a burden
10 Read electronically
14 Homophone of Aaron
15 Triple crown
16 Chunk of land
17 Maanhaar jackals
19 Boris Godunov, e.g.
20 Seven Sisters star cluster
21 Miami newspaper
23 Free of
24 Testing spot
25 Experiences a growth spurt
30 Bid adieu
33 Popeye and Olive, e.g.
34 Ominous
36 Driving aid
37 Venomous reptiles
38 Sandy-haired
39 British bloke
40 Legal point
41 Self-reproach
42 Jackie Evancho's asset
43 Christian in *The Good Shepherd*
45 Swell
47 Slip into
48 Activity
49 Did windows on Halloween
52 "Monopoly" avenue
57 Toledo's lake
58 "The Eagle" poet
60 Skier's wear
61 Cyber-sales
62 Muppet saxophonist
63 "The Memory of Trees" singer
64 Velvety flower
65 Muffs

DOWN

1 Stack
2 Kazakhstan river
3 Old Roman coins
4 Hearth accessories
5 Conflicting
6 Floor covering
7 Restrooms, in Britain
8 "___ You Sincere?"
9 Window part
10 Little despot
11 2007 Cy Young winner
12 Asian Sea
13 Geek
18 Remains
22 "Waiting for the Robert ___"
25 Celebrities
26 Golf club part
27 "Clumsy me!"
28 Wrinkly tangelo

29 *1984* laborer
30 Blu-ray predecessor
31 Wince, maybe
32 Apache abode
35 Picnic crashers
38 Pricker
39 Settle
41 Hackman in *Runaway Jury*
42 *Barbarella* director
44 Kansas city
46 With no trace of panic
49 Dotted, in heraldry
50 North African seaport
51 Low-pitched
52 "'Cuz ___": Pink
53 Director Buñuel
54 ___ about (roughly)
55 *Young Frankenstein* flunky
56 Speedy jets of yore
59 H-shaped letter

★★★ BrainSnack®—Token Effort

On which number should the black token be placed in section D?

A				B				C				D		
5	21	8		5	21	8		5	21	8		5	21	8
		1		16	13	1		16	13	1		16	13	1
9	26	7		9	26	7		9	26	7		9	26	
6	20	22		6	20			6	20	22		6	20	22
12	10	11		12	10	11		12	10	11		12	10	11
2	27	17		2	27	17		2	27			2	27	17
23	18	4		23	18	4		23	18	4		23	18	4
14	19	24		14	19	24			19	24		14	19	24
15	25	3		15		3		15	25	3		15	25	3

ONE LETTER LESS OR MORE

The word on the right side contains the letters of the word on the left side plus or minus the letter in the middle. One letter is already in the right place.

G A N G S T E R -G ☐ ☐ ☐ A ☐ ☐ ☐

★ Fruit

All the words are hidden vertically, horizontally or diagonally—in both directions. The letters that remain unused form a sentence from left to right.

```
T N A I R U D H E D I M F F E
R E Y N O L E M N C E G E B E
T W R A Y A T I P D E I E N V
H O R N E D M E L O N F E G E
T A E B E L T A M A R I L L O
E H H S A C R A S P B E R R Y
L Y C H E E T T N D M A N G O
I F S A V O C A D O R U U I A
M P O M E L O U R T I A E Y Y
E S D V A P A Q G I V G A R C
U E A A M N D M D A N P R U I
E P B E B N D U E A A E R W J
M B R S A O K K R P H R I N U
N A A P R I C O T C A K H O J
D N B O E P W Y R N O R U M U
A A L O L O O K T L A T G E B
T N T U L E T S I N A C H L E
E A M I A O N G Q U I N C E S
```

DURIAN
FIG
GRAPE
GUAVA
HORNED MELON
JUJUBE
KIWI
KORLAN
KUMQUAT
LEMON
LIME
LYCHEE
MABOLO
MANGO
MEDLAR
MELON
NECTARINE
ORANGE
PAPAYA
PEACH
PITAYA
PLUM
POMELO
QUINCE
RASPBERRY
TAMARILLO

AMBARELLA	BANANA	CHERRY
APRICOT	BARBADOS CHERRY	CURRANT
AVOCADO	CANISTEL	DATE

UNCANNY TURN

Rearrange the letters of the word below to form a cognate anagram, one which is related or connected in meaning to the original phrase. The answer can be one or more words.

ICE CIRCLET CHART

★★ Santa Players by Cindy Wheeler

ACROSS

1 Spare tire
5 Playing hard ____ (being coy)
10 Hybrid citrus fruit
14 Adjutant
15 Ancient Greek coins
16 Fall fruit
17 Cambodian currency
18 Turkish rug
19 Scholarly book
20 Meted (out)
22 Revered
24 Sleepwear
27 Resist letting go
28 Bakery enticements
29 Field mouse
30 Aliens
33 *Real Time* host Bill
34 Stag party participants
35 Buddhist monastery
36 Aquatic eagles
37 Eagle's weapon
38 In-basket item
39 Hang back
40 Errand boy
41 Irish tenor Tynan
42 From ____ Z (totally)
43 Irradiate
44 Wick holder
45 Nebraska metropolis
47 Taken down a notch
48 Hat for Mike Hammer
50 Get the picture
51 Trees in an O'Neill title
52 Nostril
54 Taking care of business
58 Wings, to Caesar
59 Kevin in *Dave*
60 Rochon in *Boomerang*
61 Beautiful people
62 Torpedoes
63 Pup's cry

DOWN

1 Distant
2 CIV - II
3 Suffix for lemon
4 Witches
5 *The Alice B. ____ Cookbook*
6 Awards for some plays
7 Gift of the Magi
8 *There Will Be Blood* preacher
9 *The Santa Clause* star
10 *Dragon's Teeth* author Sinclair
11 *Santa Baby* star
12 Evening-gown fabric
13 Full of fury
21 Epps of *House*
23 Goes out
24 Anderson in *Borat!*
25 Mount in Genesis
26 *Rudolph the Red-Nosed Reindeer* star
27 Laser printer option
29 Jeeves, for one
31 "Chili today, hot ____"
32 Blitzed
34 Godfather's group
37 *The Polar Express* star
38 Game with red hotels
40 Wheel with teeth
41 Dodge trucks
44 Desists
46 Exodus leader
47 Quaff
48 Notable act
49 Fashion magazine
50 Mild reaction to a joke
53 Rubina in *Slumdog Millionaire*
55 Miss-named
56 Unable to play, maybe
57 Attention getter

★★ Number Cluster

Complete the grid by constituting adjoining clusters that consist of as many cubes as the number on the cubes. At cube 5, for instance, you will have to make a five-cube cluster. Two or more figure cubes of the same value belong to the same cluster. You can only place your cubes along horizontal and/or vertical lines.

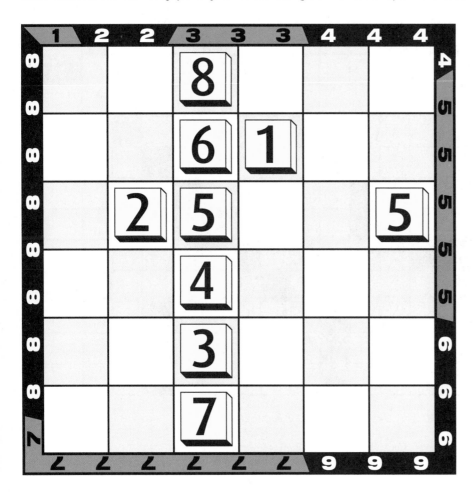

DOODLE PUZZLE

A doodle puzzle is a combination of images, letters and/or numbers that represent a word or a concept. If you cannot solve a doodle puzzle, do not look at the answer right away. Think hard—and outside the box.

★★ BrainSnack®—Letter Logic

Cross off all pairs of letters that satisfy a certain logic. Which two letters are left over?

CONNECT TWO

An oxymoron is a combination of seemingly contradictory or incongruous words, such as "Science Fiction" (Science means "knowledge or study dealing with facts or truth" while Fiction means "an imagined or invented creation"). Connect the words with meanings that oppose each other and make oxymorons.

SECOND	BREAK
TRUE	GUEST
UNINVITED	BEST
STUDY	STORY

★★ Holidays by Cindy Wheeler

ACROSS

1 Christian of fashion
5 Where Greek met Greek
11 Popular sandwich
14 Mingle-mangle
15 Like teal
16 "That makes me happy!"
17 U.S. holiday in October
19 Plow through powder
20 Lord, or his subject
21 Typewriter part
23 Las Vegas naturals
26 Shizuoka sash
27 Snobs
30 Overcharges
33 Diplomacies
34 Tie-dye alternative
36 Michele of *Glee*
37 Place
38 Peer's title
39 Geeky sort
40 John ___ Lennon
41 Like some YouTube videos
42 Spokes, e.g.
43 Neptune moon
45 Numbers
47 "___ a small world ..."
48 Form into a sac
49 Noisy fight
52 Guardian spirits
54 Assistance
55 U.S. holiday in November
60 New Zealand parrot
61 Wryly humorous
62 Red-tag event
63 British isle
64 Far from flustered
65 Brainstorm

DOWN

1 "What's up, ___?": Bugs Bunny
2 Nobelist UN agency
3 Fossil fuel
4 Casino wheel game
5 Convent superior
6 Drain sound
7 Yorkshire river
8 Purge
9 PDQ relative
10 *The Merchant of Venice* usurer
11 French National Day
12 Dam product
13 Slender
18 Revealing skirts
22 Arabic robe
23 Assails
24 Jerry's friend on *Seinfeld*
25 Canadian holiday in May
28 Lift on the slopes
29 Popular kitchen wrap
30 Do wrong
31 Risky situations
32 Cruel one
35 Colombian port
38 eBay offer
39 Daffodils and jonquils
41 Face to face
42 Kidney enzyme
44 And so forth
46 Danger
49 Charlatan
50 100 Cambodian sen
51 Moisture-free
52 Wilder in *Blazing Saddles*
53 Ireland, in verse
56 Rocky pinnacle
57 Will Smith, to Willow
58 Malt liquor
59 Pro vote

★★★ Sport Maze

Draw the shortest way from the ball to the goal. You can only move along
vertical and horizontal lines, not along diagonal lines. The figure on each square
indicates the number of squares the ball must be moved in the same direction.
You can change direction at each stop.

5	1	5	4	4	1
5	1	1	4	4	2
1	3	3	3	3	4
5	4	3	○	1	5
3	2	4	3	1	5
2	1	2	5	4	4

FRIENDS?

What do the following words have in common?

ACRE BAND MASS LINE MESS RAMP PILGRIM PERCENT

★★ Word Sudoku

Complete the grid so that each row, each column and each 3 x 3 frame contains the nine letters from the black box below. The hidden nine-letter word is in the diagonal from top left to bottom right.

A	B	C	E	I	K	R	S	T

		C		A	T	E	R	B
E		K						
	A							
				K	S		A	C
	C			R		S		
	S	I		T				
	R			S		A	I	
				E	B		S	

SANDWICH

What five-letter word belongs between the word at left and the word at right, so that the first and second word, and the second and third word, each form a common compound word or phrase?

GRAND _ _ _ _ _ PIPE

★★ Yippee! by Maggie Ellis

ACROSS
1 Guinness in *Scrooge*
5 Flees town
10 Barely open
14 Beauty pageant wear
15 Serf of ancient Sparta
16 Casual Friday shirt
17 Edgar Allan Poe poem
19 On a whale watch
20 Incomparable
21 Did a woodcut
23 Lisbon cat
24 Job's accuser
25 Harness horses
28 Eggs request
31 Earthy pigment
32 With eyes wide open
33 Drink with crumpets
34 Director Buñuel
35 Keeps an eye on
36 Bric-a-___
37 S&L machine
38 Sidewalk show
39 Enforcement power
40 Working again
42 Pick of the litter
43 *Delta of Venus* author Nin
44 Danson and Turner
45 Lock horns
47 Broadway houses
51 Smoky mist
52 *Through the Looking-Glass* character
54 City on the Oka River
55 Dangle the carrot
56 "___ Stung": Presley
57 Roger in *Nicholas Nickelby*
58 Better equipped
59 *The Water Horse* loch

DOWN
1 Rush!
2 Diane in *Judge Dredd*
3 Old English slave
4 Cavalry horses
5 Some linens
6 Michael on *That '70s Show*
7 Woes
8 "Annabel Lee" poet
9 Pittsburgh team
10 Attack helicopter
11 U2 album (with *The*)
12 Downwind, to Popeye
13 "The ___ Not Taken": Frost
18 Bugle sound
22 Become weary
24 Get out of
25 Arctic bear
26 Shrill
27 Man's closest kin
28 Held the title to
29 Acts as usher
30 Sports boat
32 Buenos ___
35 "Naughty" operetta heroine
36 *How to Ruin Your Life* author
38 Tehran coin
39 Wave type
41 Backers
42 Tributary
44 "___ Dreams": Heart
45 God with a hammer
46 Berne's river
47 Dabbling duck
48 Razor feature
49 Speed Wagons
50 Volleyball stats
53 Spider snare

★★ Sudoku

Fill in the grid so that each row, each column and each 3 x 3 frame contains every number from 1 to 9.

		1	9					4
	2		7	6	3		1		5
		9	5		2		7	8
				9	6		1	7
5	7	2	1				4	
			5			3	
	5					6	
9		8		6				

DOUBLETALK

★★ **BrainSnack®—Alphabet**

Which letter is colored incorrectly?

LETTERBLOCKS

Move the letterblocks around so that words are formed on top and below that you can associate with clothes.

★★★ Disney Filmfest by John M. Samson

ACROSS

1 Tykes
5 Dispositions
10 They can help if you're short
14 Maui feast
15 Temporarily shelved
16 Workplace
17 1950 Disney film
19 Golden Globe winner Ward
20 "And ___ fine fiddle had he ..."
21 "___ of Gold": Sting
23 Pertinence
26 LuPone or Page
27 Damsel's post-rescue remark
28 Fatiguing
31 French seaport
32 Wino
33 Suffix for pater
34 Old Turin coins
35 Peter in a tongue twister
36 Like ___ in a candy shop
37 Hot time in Paris
38 Make a payment
39 Safari figure
40 Autocratic
42 Original *SNL* cast member Gilda
43 Checked out
44 Disparages
45 "Time After Time" singer Cyndi
47 Theater feature
48 Vicinity
49 1995 Disney film
54 Elwes in *The Princess Bride*
55 ___ a dozen
56 Penny
57 Joy Adamson's lioness
58 Rock bottom
59 Wee whirlpool

DOWN

1 Pampering
2 Yes, in Montreal
3 Copper-toned
4 Khartoum denizens
5 Greater
6 Unusual blokes
7 Like unwashed hair
8 Year in St. Martin's papacy
9 Sailor
10 Desirable things
11 1994 Disney film
12 Foundry form
13 Fat farms
18 Tennis legend Chris
22 Cato's way
23 Sauntered
24 Fool's gold
25 1977 Disney film
26 Calibrated tube
28 Fuel for a debate
29 Ship's first voyage
30 Church officers
32 Like Caspar Milquetoast
35 1953 Disney film
36 Papal interview
38 Scent of a woman
39 Modesto winery
41 Hawaiian fruit
42 More impetuous
44 Where Dolphins play
45 Spike the punch
46 Inland sea of Asia
47 LSD
50 Psychic in *Ghost*
51 Director Demme
52 "___ so it goes"
53 Pigs' digs

★ Spot the Differences

Find the nine differences in the image on the right.

CHANGE ONE

Change one letter in each of these two words to form a common two-word phrase. There may be more than one possible answer.

BUNG TO

★ Horoscope

Fill in the grid so that every row, every column and every frame of six boxes contains six different symbols: health, work, money, happiness, family and love. Look at the row or column that corresponds with your sign of the zodiac and find out which of the six symbols are important for you today. The symbols appear in increasing order of importance (1–6). It's up to you to translate the meaning of each symbol to your specific situation.

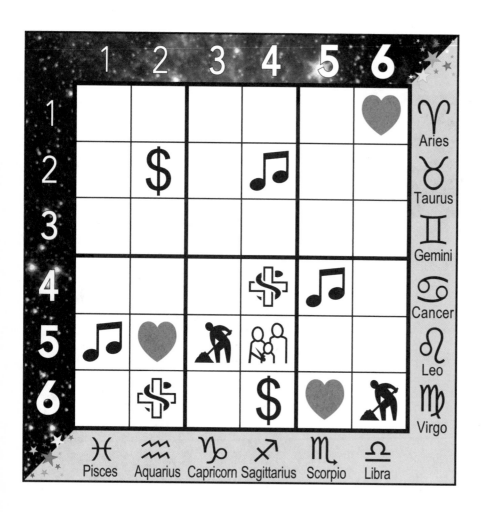

REPOSITION PREPOSITION

Unscramble ACES INFO and find a three-word preposition.

★★ Futoshiki

Fill in the 5 x 5 grid with the numbers from 1 to 5 once per row and column, while following the greater than/lesser than symbols shown. There is only one valid solution that can be reached through logic and clear thinking alone!

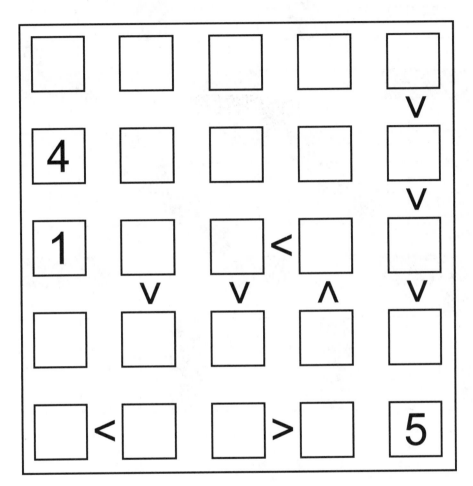

CONNECT TWO

An oxymoron is a combination of seemingly contradictory or incongruous words, such as "Science Fiction" (Science means "knowledge or study dealing with facts or truth" while Fiction means "an imagined or invented creation"). Connect the words with meanings that oppose each other and make oxymorons.

AWFULLY	WOOL
STEEL	HOLIDAY
WORKING	ADULT
YOUNG	GOOD

★★★ Advanced Geometry by Karen Peterson

ACROSS

1 ___ Rica
6 Road Runner's sound
10 Fictional whaler
14 Scarf or race track
15 Shrinking Asian sea
16 Electronics giant
17 June birthstone
18 Fatigue
19 Overdue
20 Classified files leaked by Daniel Ellsberg
23 "No man ___ island"
24 Calais–Paris direction
25 Aesop's stories
28 Wanders aimlessly
33 Translucent gems
34 Sprinkles
35 Caesar's 151
36 Babysitting nickname
37 Fabricated
38 Habeas corpus, e.g.
39 Erving of basketball
40 Whale food
41 "El Capitan" composer
42 Idealists
44 Curling wave
45 RSA political party
46 ___ fond farewell
47 Opium-producing area of Asia
54 Fiesta
55 Earring spot
56 Barnstormer
57 Camaro model
58 Drake in *Cheers*
59 Form of oxygen
60 Apollo's instrument
61 Like crabapples
62 Small flycatcher

DOWN

1 Fearless Fosdick's creator
2 Hosea in the Douay Bible
3 Computerized photo
4 Mexican snack
5 Map holders
6 Majorette's stick
7 ___ *go bragh!*
8 Tombstone marshal
9 Amiable
10 Snoozing
11 Frost
12 Aardvark's dinner
13 "Toodle-oo"
21 Sunoco product
22 Chi followers
25 Ballet bend
26 Unconnected
27 Hillbilly music maker
28 Follows
29 Moon marking
30 Benchwarmer
31 Beethoven's *Für* ___
32 Lute of India
34 Devastation
37 Jewelry item
38 Chase skirts
40 Benevolent
41 Belly-wash
43 London's Crystal ___
44 LI doubled
46 Spiner of *Star Trek: TNG*
47 SpongeBob's pet snail
48 Swan genus
49 Smoked salmon
50 Lift on the slopes
51 Shine
52 Unpartnered
53 Derby winner Lil ___
54 Grissom of *CSI*

★ Home, Garden and Kitchen

All the words are hidden vertically, horizontally or diagonally—in both directions. The letters that remain unused form a sentence from left to right.

```
G T O O T H B R U S H A R R D
G R A T E R E E N T I O E O R
E L A C S L S L A R E R W N E
I R O N I N G B O A R D O O M
C E I L I N G M O P T R M N M
P O R E C S K I M M E R N I I
S H I O N E Q H M T U I W F R
P L E V O H S T S O M E A W T
N R T B U T T U H E O C L O S
Y O L E A F B L O W E R K R S
R Z S P A T U L A C M C B R A
A A U Q S T S T L B I P E A R
K R C U U E E O R P I Z O B G
E E D H B E T K H N E E D L E
U W D S A H E T C E T A N E D
M O O A I L O G W U S T U E R
F O R K P O K T E E B R E H S
I N A P T S U D S E T A N W T
```

GRATER
HOE
IRON
IRONING BOARD
LAWN MOWER
LEAF BLOWER
NEEDLE
PIN
RAKE
RAZOR
SCALE
SHOVEL
SKIMMER
SPADE
SPATULA
SQUEEGEE
THIMBLE
TOOTHBRUSH
TOOTHPICK
TWEEZERS
WHEELBARROW
WOK

BROOM
BUCKET
CEILING MOP
CHALK
DUSTBUSTER
DUSTPAN
FACE CLOTH
FORK
GRASS TRIMMER

SANDWICH

What four-letter word belongs between the word at left and the word at right, so that the first and second word, and the second and third word, each form a common compound word or phrase?

HIGH _ _ _ _ MARK

★★ Sunny Weather

Where will the sun shine? With the knowledge that each arrow points to a place where a symbol should be, can you locate the sunny spots? The symbols cannot be next to each other vertically, horizontally or diagonally. A symbol cannot be placed on top of an arrow. We show one symbol.

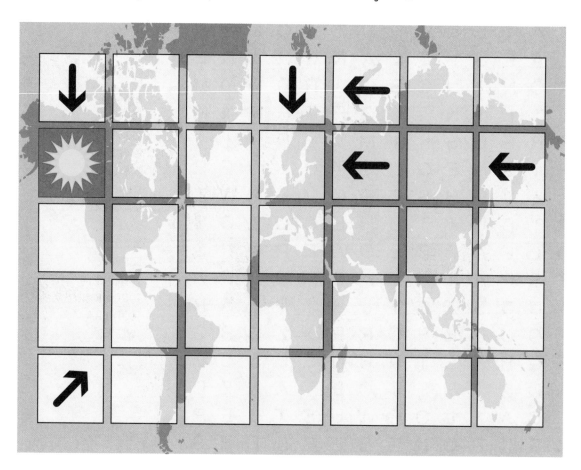

UNCANNY TURN

Rearrange the letters of the word below to form a cognate anagram, one which is related or connected in meaning to the original phrase. The answer can be one or more words.

IS TO RUN IN

★★★ Animated Films by Linda Lather

ACROSS

1 Conceited
5 Team bigwig
10 Give a bias to
14 First-rate
15 Big land animal
16 Melody
17 Martin Lawrence voices Boog here
19 Paquin of *True Blood*
20 Collective abbr.
21 *Empire March* composer
22 Hockey infraction
25 Inventory item's place
27 *Paradise Lost* angel
28 Curse
30 Einstein's birth city
33 Principles
35 Tenth Commandment sin
36 Baked good
37 Foot: Comb. form
38 Student of Socrates
40 Picnic visitor
41 Assault weapon
42 Norwegian saint
43 Band horn
46 End of a KO count
47 Foundations
49 Go by bike
50 Dixie breakfast dish
52 Get ready
54 Fried cake
56 Architect Saarinen
57 *Rise of the Planet of the ___* (2011)
58 Chris Rock voices Marty here
64 Candied tubers
65 New Zealand native
66 Piece of cake
67 "Get lost!"
68 Out of sorts
69 Sushi drink

DOWN

1 ___ Paulo
2 Cleaning tool
3 *Le Figaro* article
4 Lake Ontario feeder
5 Hill nymph
6 Pod members
7 Grafton's ___ *for Noose*
8 Roxy Music's Brian
9 Perlman in *Hellboy*
10 Play for time
11 Jack Black voices Po here
12 Sicilian resort
13 Have on
18 Walking pole
21 Creepy
22 Production
23 "Don't move!"
24 Ellen DeGeneres voices Dory here
25 Delivered by post
26 Utter devastation
29 Latticework
31 One-dimensional
32 Grit
34 Sound at an egg toss
39 Colleen
42 Last notice
44 Beethoven wrote only one
45 States of rest
48 "Circus" singer Britney
51 Rene in *Get Shorty*
53 Mr. Philbin
54 Calendar squares
55 Colorful fish
58 Caesar's 2,100
59 Berne river
60 Cock-a-doodle-___
61 Motorist's org. in Toronto
62 Inquire
63 Deli bread

★★★ BrainSnack®—Digital Display

Which number is missing in the bottom right corner? Read the numbers per column.

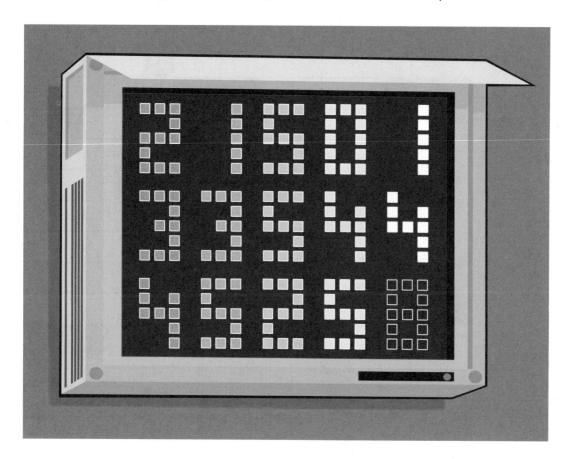

ONE LETTER LESS OR MORE

The word on the right side contains the letters of the word on the left side plus or minus the letter in the middle. One letter is already in the right place.

GARFIELD -D- F ☐☐☐☐☐☐

★★ Kakuro

Each number in a black area is the sum of the numbers that you have to enter in the next empty boxes. The empty boxes that make up the sum are called a run. The sum of the across run is written above the diagonal in the black area and the sum of the down run is written below the diagonal. Runs can only contain the numbers 1 through 9 and each number in a run can only be used once. The gray boxes only contain odd numbers and the white only even numbers.

BLOCK ANAGRAM

Form the word that is described in the brackets with the letters above the grid. Extra letters are already in the right place.

NEED DIET (sovereign)

| | N | | P | | | | N | |

★★★ Fictional Lawyers I by Mary Leonard

ACROSS

1 Blah
5 Like aged cheddar
10 *2001* extras
14 Wife of Charlie Chaplin
15 Shire in *Rocky*
16 Lyra's brightest star
17 Lawyer in *The Rainmaker*
19 Fairway club
20 Uses a ruler
21 Gets to know
23 Trying trip
24 Well-dressed
25 Large-kitchen feature
28 Court violation
31 Abides
32 Welch's grape ___
33 Heavenly altar
34 Shaving cream ingredient
35 Imprecation
36 Sale condition
37 Boy of the house
38 He led an army in the PGA
39 Painter's wear
40 Amusing icebreaker
42 Scottish clan chiefs
43 Tibetan city
44 Wintry frost
45 Miscellaneous category
47 Plans
51 Pouting expression
52 TV lawyer played by Andy Griffith
54 Kitchen scraps
55 "He's ___ nowhere man ...": Beatles
56 Romance novelist Foster
57 Squish out
58 Comes down
59 The heavens, to Atlas

DOWN

1 Campus quarters
2 Lecher
3 Time ___ half
4 Massachusetts nickname
5 Gaped
6 Salma in *Frida*
7 ___ *Well That Ends Well*
8 Brazil metropolis
9 Lingo
10 Propel a triplane
11 Erle Stanley Gardner's lawyer
12 "The Hermits" painter Schiele
13 ___ serif
18 "A Red, Red Rose" poet
22 Ending with major
24 Cacophony
25 ___ *Teenage Werewolf* (1957)
26 Sitting room
27 Lawyer in *The Simpsons*
28 Polonium discoverer
29 Vincent in *The Fly*
30 "Honey do" list items
32 Military government
35 Vaulter's hurdle
36 Texas Panhandle city
38 Jewish month
39 Commandment word
41 Fondue ingredient
42 Adds up
44 Capable of mistakes
45 1847 Melville book
46 Matador's ring mate
47 "That's ___ haven't heard!"
48 When two hands meet
49 Lampshade shade
50 Snow runners
53 Gay Nineties, e.g.

★★ Word Sudoku

Complete the grid so that each row, each column and each 3 x 3 frame contains the nine letters from the black box below. The hidden nine-letter word is in the diagonal from top left to bottom right.

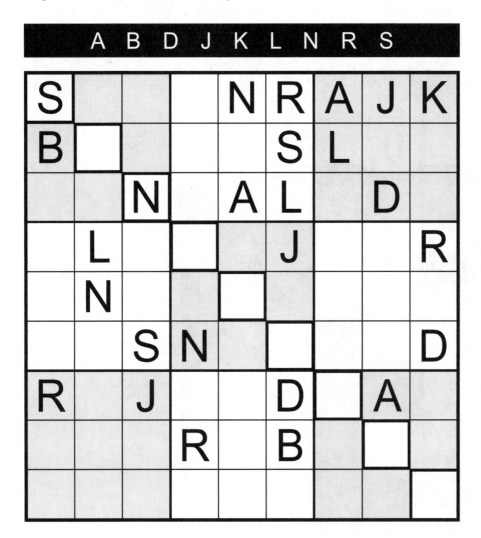

DOUBLETALK

Homophones are words that share the same pronunciation, no matter how they are spelled. If they are spelled differently then they are called heterographs. Find heterographs meaning:

NOT FANCY and A SMOOTHING TOOL

★★ Keep Going

Start on a blank square of your choice and connect as many blank squares as possible with one single continuous line. You can only connect squares along vertical and horizontal lines, not along diagonal lines. You must continue the connecting line up until the next obstacle, i.e., the rim of the box, a black square or a square that has already been used. You can change direction at any obstacle you meet. Each square can be used only once. The number of blank squares that will be left unused is marked in the upper square. There is more than one solution. We show only one solution.

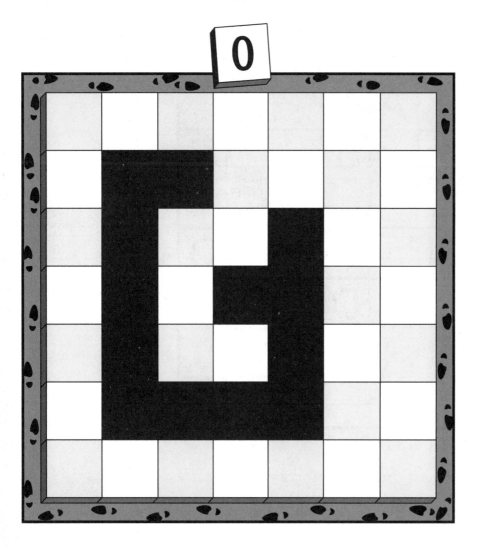

DELETE ONE

Delete one letter from MUST RANT and have an emotional outburst.

★★★ Fictional Lawyers II by Mary Leonard

ACROSS
1 Worried gait
5 One loafing
10 Yemen capital
14 Ping product
15 Nobody
16 *Beau Geste* novelist
17 Glenn Close on *Damages*
19 "I knew ___ instant ..."
20 Raises
21 Inflame
23 Happens to
26 Wise saying
27 Green, maybe
28 Sugarland number
29 Limbo must
32 Reads a bar code
33 Swiss capital
34 "Turn to Stone" band
35 Extended family
36 Jeweler's weight
37 *CSI: NY* network
38 Tattoo, slangily
39 Spin
40 George of *Star Trek*
42 Track longshot
43 Like grigs
44 Chinese noodle dish
45 Farmland units
47 Expels from a country
48 Temporary bed
50 Roper's target
51 Green emotion
52 Calista Flockhart's lawyer role
57 Oklahoma city
58 Emperor Selassie
59 Murray of tennis
60 Solitary
61 Number of Roman hills
62 Genesis creation

DOWN
1 *Great Expectations* lad
2 Parrot genus
3 Bed
4 Get on board
5 Take a hit
6 Activists
7 Storm systems
8 180° from WSW
9 Doctor with long hours
10 Go for a pitch
11 Corbin Bernsen on *L.A. Law*
12 Well-kept
13 *A Little Night Music* heroine
18 Sharp barks
22 Portal
23 Calf-length boot
24 Live oak
25 Paul Newman in *The Verdict*
26 Of hearing
28 Northern Ireland county
30 Though
31 Prepares a violin bow
33 Jumps ship
36 Wild cats
39 Used to be
40 Subject of debate
41 Microscopic shape-shifters
44 Gofers
46 Walt Frazier's nickname
47 Moriarty's creator
48 Orange throwaway
49 Part of A.D.
50 Hadrian's 554
53 Papuan port
54 Finish
55 Citrus drink
56 Indy racer St. James

★★★ Sport Maze

Draw the shortest way from the ball to the goal. You can only move along vertical and horizontal lines, not along diagonal lines. The figure on each square indicates the number of squares the ball must be moved in the same direction. You can change direction at each stop.

5	2	2	4	●	5
5	2	2	4	3	1
5	1	0	1	3	3
1	3	1	3	4	4
2	2	2	3	2	1
2	3	5	2	1	2

SANDWICH

What four-letter word belongs between the word at left and the word at right, so that the first and second word, and the second and third word, each form a common compound word or phrase?

STOCK _ _ _ _ MATE

★★★ Sudoku

Fill in the grid so that each row, each column and each 3 x 3 frame contains every number from 1 to 9.

				4				
5				4				
		4		9	2			6
		1	8		4			2
7								
	8			1			7	
	6					5		9
3	4	7						1
				6	3	2		

CONNECT TWO

An oxymoron is a combination of seemingly contradictory or incongruous words, such as "Science Fiction" (Science means "knowledge or study dealing with facts or truth" while Fiction means "an imagined or invented creation"). Connect the words with meanings that oppose each other and make oxymorons.

SAFE	EYE
BLIND	GRAND
BABY	HISTORY
MODERN	BET

★ BrainSnack®—Full Piggy

Knowing that piggy banks A, B and F are full, which fourth piggy bank (C-E) is also full?

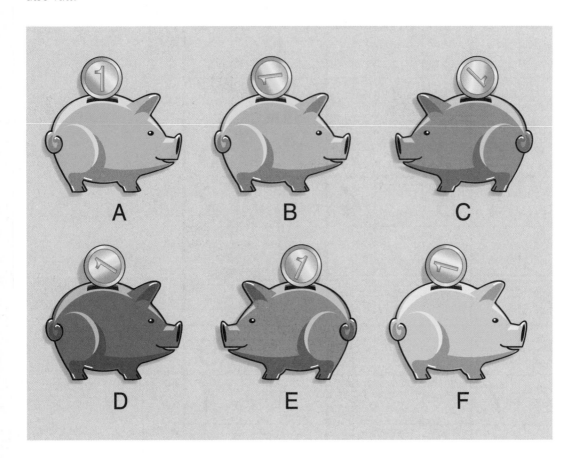

LETTERBLOCKS

Move the letterblocks around so that words are formed on top and below that you can associate with fruits.

E N H C R Y *
N R A B A A S

★★★ R&B Classics I by Michele Sayer

ACROSS

1 Cowardly Lion actor
5 Berry in *Monster's Ball*
10 "Shoo cat!"
14 Hershfield's "agent"
15 Tatum or Shaquille
16 Lombardy lake
17 "What's Going On" singer
19 Love deity
20 Went to an event
21 Roaches and rodents
23 Bavarian river
24 Plaster painting
25 Postpones
28 Resigned
31 Raise on high
32 ___ *Carlo* (2011)
33 Trireme item
34 Dobbin's dad
35 Like a bad steak
36 Jason's ship
37 Lookout point
38 Clubs for Luke Donald
39 Marina features
40 *Peaceful Warrior* star
42 Cash prizes
43 Braid
44 Back muscles
45 Crafty plan
47 Falsify
51 Corey in *License to Drive*
52 "Hit the Road Jack" singer
54 Russian Art Deco designer
55 Mast pole
56 Ditto, in footnotes
57 Musher's vehicle
58 Sister of Euterpe
59 Cornbread

DOWN

1 Himalayan priest
2 Blind as ___
3 Dixieland trumpeter Al
4 Bugle call
5 Element and Pilot
6 Madden
7 Bullets, slangily
8 Minstrel's song
9 Junior grade
10 Uncommon
11 "Easy" group
12 Mine, in Montreal
13 Ripped
18 Magnified map
22 Pilate's "Behold!"
24 Hymnal contents
25 Seed coat
26 Self-evident principle
27 "Let the Music Play" singer
28 Dracula-like Muppet
29 Tidal bore
30 Smeltery refuse
32 Roger in *Moonraker*
35 Travel across
36 Simple runway
38 Mosque priest
39 ___ stop to (ends)
41 Looked
42 Afghan language
44 Lawful
45 "The Liner ___ a Lady": Kipling
46 Sagan or Icahn
47 *Deathtrap* victim
48 "Fantasy" singer Nova
49 Young adult
50 Mrs. Hoggett in *Babe*
53 Mo. in which the Civil War started

★ Light

All the words are hidden vertically, horizontally or diagonally—in both directions. The letters that remain unused form a sentence from left to right.

```
L  A  N  G  I  S  L  O  W  B  E  N  E  R  G
R  S  Y  R  L  S  P  O  T  L  I  G  H  T  I
P  E  T  R  O  L  E  U  M  U  G  H  R  T  B
T  U  S  E  L  M  B  S  L  B  A  S  E  T  L
O  H  N  I  A  Y  A  P  A  R  A  F  F  I  N
G  E  G  R  S  R  T  N  N  E  G  O  L  A  H
T  H  A  I  N  T  I  E  T  I  N  C  E  A  N
E  D  E  S  L  C  A  N  F  I  E  N  C  T  O
L  A  L  A  D  D  I  N  N  A  C  E  T  W  M
E  F  F  I  C  I  E  N  C  Y  S  S  O  O  U
C  D  W  H  I  C  H  L  M  E  E  D  R  I  R
T  E  I  S  T  R  E  E  T  L  A  M  P  L  T
R  F  U  S  E  A  N  S  D  H  F  L  E  L  C
I  L  X  W  O  E  R  N  S  L  U  B  U  A  E
C  A  E  D  Y  N  A  M  O  N  E  L  B  M  P
I  S  N  S  A  C  R  E  G  T  H  U  A  P  S
T  E  O  X  A  W  S  E  E  B  R  L  F  O  W
Y  R  N  A  R  C  L  A  M  P  F  N  O  U  T
```

FLAME
FUEL
FUSE
HALOGEN
LASER
LED LIGHT
OIL LAMP
PARAFFIN
PETROLEUM
PLUNGE
REFLECTOR
RESISTANCE
ROMANTIC
SAFETY
SHADOW
SIGNAL
SPECTRUM
SPOTLIGHT
STEARIN
STREETLAMP
XENON

ALADDIN
ARC LAMP
BEESWAX

BULB
CANDLE
DYNAMO

EDISON
EFFICIENCY
ELECTRICITY

CHANGE ONE

Change one letter in each of these two words to form a common two-word phrase. There may be more than one possible answer.

RIPE CREAM

★★★ BrainSnack®—Missing Middle

Which nucleus (1–6) should replace the question mark?

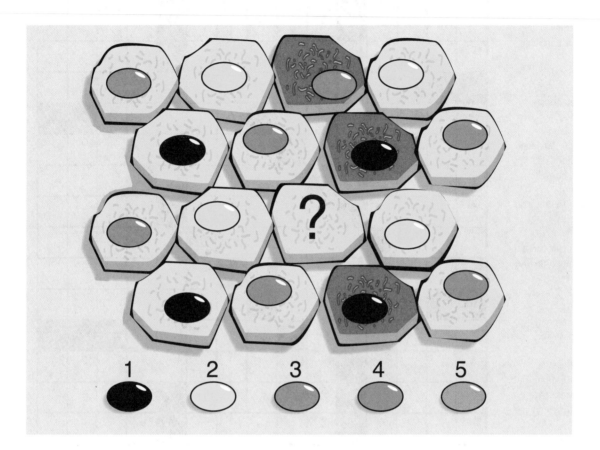

DOODLE PUZZLE

A doodle puzzle is a combination of images, letters and/or numbers that represent a word or a concept. If you cannot solve a doodle puzzle, do not look at the answer right away. Think hard—and outside the box.

★★★ R&B Classics II by Michele Sayer

ACROSS

1 Creole stew
5 "I Got ___ ": Croce
10 Makes a pick
14 Tree for a partridge
15 Daft
16 Andean land
17 "Soul Man" duo
19 Age after Bronze
20 Stripped
21 Areas of land
23 Leaves the rat race
26 Like Italian subs
27 Home of Cornell University
28 *My Cousin Vinny* star
31 Bill O'Reilly's ___-*Spin Zone*
32 Tends to the socks
33 Allie's fiancé in *The Notebook*
34 Hits with a laser
35 Dirt
36 Word on a penny
37 Chemical suffix
38 Cuckoo
39 Bob and weave
40 They're on guard duty
42 Horseshoes feat
43 Billy, Nanny and the kids?
44 Baltimore's time zone
45 House of worship
47 "Curiouser and curiouser!" utterer
48 Mop, perhaps
49 "Blueberry Hill" singer
54 Elizabeth II's daughter
55 Loosen laces
56 Figurehead location
57 Gridiron throw
58 Longtime "Today" host
59 Soothe the savage beast

DOWN

1 Roman goddess of plenty
2 New Zealand parrot
3 Bighorn with big horns
4 Exquisite equines
5 Petkovic of tennis
6 Peter Paul Rubens subjects
7 Ever so slightly
8 *Jersey Shore* network
9 Upper canines
10 Sedative drug
11 "When a Man Loves a Woman" singer
12 Move briskly
13 Balls of fire
18 Drug cop
22 Emulates LL Cool J
23 Round crackers
24 Flammable gas
25 "Earth Angel" group
26 Jerry Seinfeld's TV dad
28 Throws for a loop
29 Large eel
30 Summer office worker
32 URLs
35 True to one's word
36 Disdain
38 Bric-a-___
39 Summer music
41 Tico of Bon Jovi
42 Marauder
44 Miss Marley of rhyme
45 Fellow
46 *The English Patient* heroine
47 Island off Alaska
50 Japanese airline
51 Tax shelter
52 ___ de plume
53 Run up a tab

★★ Sudoku X

Fill in the grid so that each row, each column and each 3 x 3 frame contains every number from 1 to 9. The two main diagonals of the grid also contain every number from 1 to 9.

				9				
3								
	1		6		4			
		8			7		4	
6	4			1	5	2		
2	9	1		3				6
			3	7			9	
1		6	8	4		5		7
9	7						2	4

FRIENDS?

What do the following words have in common?

MOLECULAR CHROME PHONIC GRAPH CHORD FUEL

★★★ Binairo

Complete the grid with zeros and ones until there are 6 zeros and 6 ones in every row and every column. No more than two of the same number can be next to or under each other. Rows or columns with exactly the same content are not allowed. There is only one valid solution.

					O						
	I		O					I			
		O		I							
					O						
				I					I		
							I			O	
I	O		I	I		O					
				I				O			O
		I	I								O
				I				I			
	O			I							O
	O		I			O			I	O	

UNCANNY TURN

Rearrange the letters of the word below to form a cognate anagram, one which is related or connected in meaning to the original phrase. The answer can be one or more words.

NATURE HINTED

★★★ Crazy Quilt by Maggie Ellis

ACROSS
1 "My treat!"
5 Holy Tibetans
10 Mix
14 Ball-shaped hammer part
15 *Z* actress Papas
16 Comment of understanding
17 Elementary school subject
19 Club for Graeme McDowell
20 Bracco in *GoodFellas*
21 Grade-school staples
23 Western ski resort
24 Italian seaport
25 Sea urchin's defense
28 Day named after a Roman god
31 Rep. Pelosi
32 Robot of Hebrew lore
33 Bleat
34 "The Raven" opener
35 Was sensitive
36 Dr. Jung
37 *Deep Space Nine* changeling
38 Dixie breakfast dish
39 78-card deck
40 Running of the bulls city
42 Williams of tennis
43 Squeeze together
44 Initiation
45 Many cons
47 Overshoes
51 El Paso college
52 Oppressive
54 "The Bird Cage" artist
55 Encore!
56 He directed Marlon
57 Make eyes at
58 Android
59 "The Farmer in the ___"

DOWN
1 Gem for a Libra
2 Franco in *Camelot*
3 Israeli premier (1969–74)
4 Portal
5 Ceilings
6 Sports venue
7 Allocate (out)
8 Darth Vader, as a boy
9 Hidden
10 Sinbad, e.g.
11 Worn
12 "Either it ___ it isn't!"
13 Howard and Reagan
18 Jack in *The Wizard of Oz*
22 *E pluribus* ___
24 Howling winds
25 Meddler
26 Jack Black *Kung Fu* role
27 Sketchy
28 Rather, informally
29 Brother of Moses
30 WWII conference site
32 Improvements
35 Goalpost part
36 Embraced
38 Country singer Campbell
39 What Sitting Bull spoke
41 Correct
42 Tight-lipped
44 Bose product
45 Biodiesel, for one
46 French 101 verb
47 Snatch
48 Bagel center
49 Pianist Gilels
50 Circus pinniped
53 Italian actor Tognazzi

★★ Keep Going

Start on a blank square of your choice and connect as many blank squares as possible with one single continuous line. You can only connect squares along vertical and horizontal lines, not along diagonal lines. You must continue the connecting line up until the next obstacle, i.e., the rim of the box, a black square or a square that has already been used. You can change direction at any obstacle you meet. Each square can be used only once. The number of blank squares that will be left unused is marked in the upper square. There is more than one solution. We show only one solution.

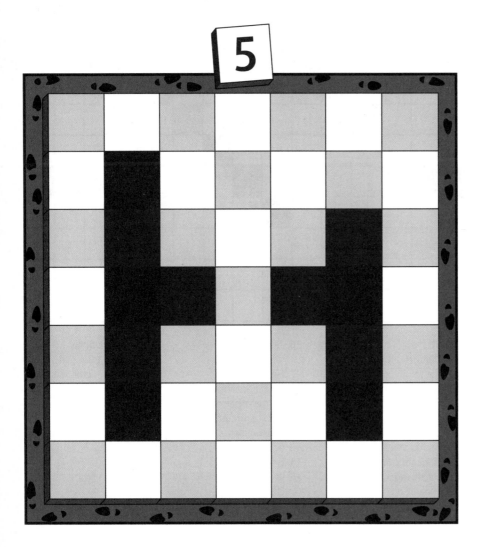

REPOSITION PREPOSITION

Unscramble SAS AFAR and find a three-word preposition.

★ BrainSnack®—Party Hardy

Which party hat (1–5) isn't part of the series?

DOUBLETALK

Homophones are words that share the same pronunciation, no matter how they are spelled. If they are spelled differently then they are called heterographs. Find heterographs meaning:

HELPERS and THE HELP

★★★ Eclectic Group by Maggie Ellis

ACROSS

1 Act as accomplice
5 Gleaming
10 Dame with lilac-colored hair
14 Secure tightly
15 Cry of accomplishment
16 Some August births
17 Morales of *NYPD Blue*
18 Despicable ones
19 Siouan language
20 Ill-natured
22 Sunflower State capital
24 Yahoos lack it
25 Medieval violin
26 Also-rans
29 Baptize
32 Made a choice
33 Sherlock's love
34 O'Neill sea play
35 ___ *Torino* (2008)
36 Clove hitch and granny
37 Declare affirmatively
38 Suffix for confident
39 Humongous
40 Change a bill
41 Wyoming capital
43 Doctoral paper
44 Mrs. Homer Simpson
45 Paddington, for one
46 Sissy in *The River*
48 Dick Cheney's successor
52 Courtroom affirmation
53 Bad blood
55 *Sex and the ___* (2008)
56 Banjo feature
57 Majestic
58 Texas Hold'em stake
59 1979 Polanski film
60 Cupidity
61 Orderly

DOWN

1 Guinness in *Kafka*
2 Wild party
3 Isaac's hairy son
4 Triskaidekaphobia fear
5 Top floors
6 Poltergeist
7 Mother of Reuben and Simeon
8 Baggage tag for O'Hare
9 Oaters
10 Marries quietly
11 Hammer and Spade
12 Cozy spot
13 Off shore
21 Cooking fat
23 Tony's relative
25 Scarlett's love in *Gone With the Wind*
26 Reasoning science
27 OWN chairman
28 No-win situations
29 *Macbeth* soothsayer
30 Greek tennis star Daniilidou
31 Cybergeeks
33 Empty-headed
36 Ann Darrow's simian friend
37 *An ___ in Paris* (1951)
39 Richard in *Shall We Dance?*
40 Starbuck's skipper
42 Palm Beach sights
43 Swarmed
45 Round bread loaf
46 Far from stern
47 Remove rind
48 See eye to eye
49 Break bread
50 "At Last" singer James
51 Nikita's negative
54 Droning beetle

★★★ Sport Maze

Draw the shortest way from the ball to the goal. You can only move along vertical and horizontal lines, not along diagonal lines. The figure on each square indicates the number of squares the ball must be moved in the same direction. You can change direction at each stop.

5	2	5	3	3	5
1	3	2	4	3	1
2	4	2	2	2	4
5	2	0	0	4	
4	1	4	1	3	3
5	2	1	1	4	4

CONNECT TWO

An oxymoron is a combination of seemingly contradictory or incongruous words, such as "Science Fiction" (Science means "knowledge or study dealing with facts or truth" while Fiction means "an imagined or invented creation"). Connect the words with meanings that oppose each other and make oxymorons.

SIT　　DOWN
CLIMB　　UNSEEN
CONSTANT　　UP
SIGHT　　CHANGE

★★ Sudoku X

Fill in the grid so that each row, each column and each 3 x 3 frame contains every number from 1 to 9. The two main diagonals of the grid also contain every number from 1 to 9.

1	3		7	8	4	5		2
4		2			3	7		
6				2	5			3
	2			1			3	5
	9			3				4
	6							
	7					2	8	
				5			4	
						3		

SANDWICH

What four-letter word belongs between the word at left and the word at right, so that the first and second word, and the second and third word, each form a common compound word or phrase?

F I S H _ _ _ _ Y A R D

★★★ A Night at the Opera by Karen Peterson

ACROSS

1 Rogan josh meat
5 Strip
9 Paul of *Lonesome Dove*
14 Bread spread
15 Sideburns, e.g.
16 Bring to joy
17 Verdi opera of 1851
19 Pledges
20 Misrepresent
21 Flowers used in chains
23 Old Roman coins
24 Campus marchers
25 Dip stick?
28 Hudson in *Dreamgirls*
32 Inedible orange
33 Spy Mata ___
34 History Muse
35 Giant with 511 homers
36 Training staff
37 Edible ginseng plant
38 Handed-down beliefs
40 Holiday preceders
41 Renaissance song
43 Covered with stars
45 Records another's song
46 Poetic glen
47 Indy driver Luyendyk
48 "Open, Sesame!" sayer
51 Tell the story
55 Kicks into nets
56 Verdi opera of 1867
58 Tosses in a chip
59 Running wild
60 SUVs
61 All set
62 Tampa Bay team
63 Swelling

DOWN

1 "My Sweet ___": Harrison
2 Others, to Ovid
3 Digital camera units
4 Smuggle
5 Spanish wine
6 Cappuccino cousin
7 River islet
8 Trampled down
9 French Foreign ___
10 Springy
11 Mozart opera of 1791 (with *The*)
12 To ___ (exactly)
13 Cher's *Burlesque* role
18 Longest river in France
22 Links legend Palmer
25 Puts on ice
26 Prohibit

27 Verdi opera of 1853
28 Beyond blasé
29 Wanders
30 Pillow stuffing
31 Sources
33 Include
36 Paparazzi target
39 Made possible
41 *The Cutting Edge* star Kelly
42 Surplus printing
44 Vitreous
45 Breaks a code
47 Be a pain in the neck
48 Pastry thickener
49 Solitary
50 Jewish month
52 Vocal range
53 Nailed obliquely
54 Latin 101 verb
57 German grandma

★★ BrainSnack®—Latin Rhythm

Which maraca (1–6) does not belong?

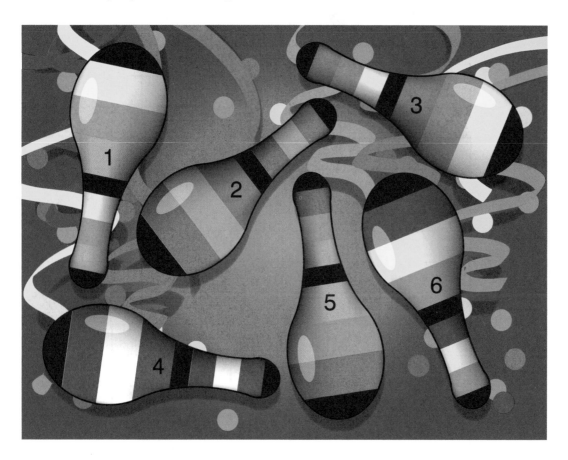

BLOCK ANAGRAM

Form the word that is described in the brackets with the letters above the grid. Extra letters are already in the right place.

DISTANCE *(nominees)*

			D		A		

★ Word Pyramid

Each word in the pyramid has the letters of the word above it, plus a new letter.

A

(1) expresses position
(2) furry, domesticated mammal
(3) informal conversation
(4) betray
(5) Swiss house
(6) honorable
(7) having a well proportioned body

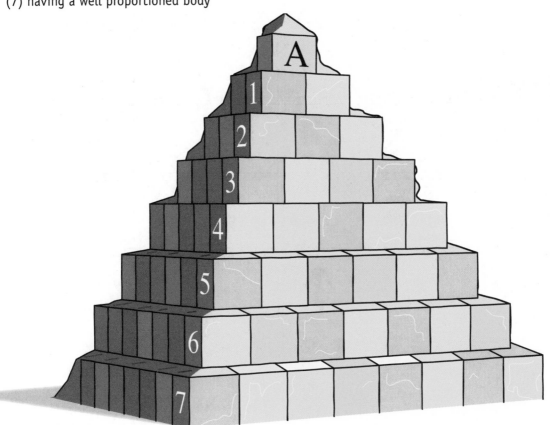

DELETE ONE

Delete one letter from TO RECANT SIR and find a withdrawal.

★★ Sunny Weather

Where will the sun shine? With the knowledge that each arrow points to a place where a symbol should be, can you locate the sunny spots? The symbols cannot be next to each other vertically, horizontally or diagonally. A symbol cannot be placed on top of an arrow. We show one symbol.

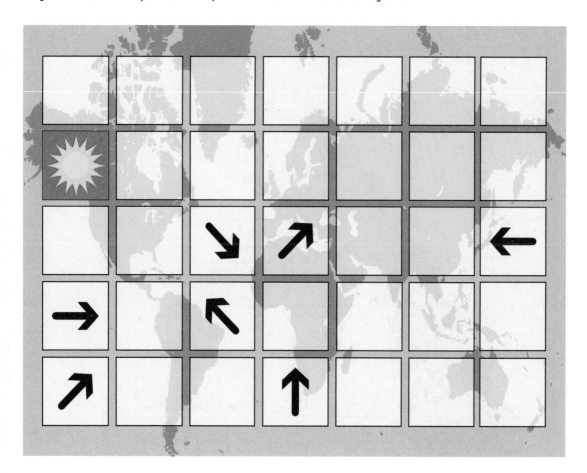

ONE LETTER LESS OR MORE

The word on the right side contains the letters of the word on the left side plus or minus the letter in the middle. One letter is already in the right place.

B A C T E R I A +L ▢ ▢ L ▢ ▢ ▢ ▢ ▢

★★★★ **Themeless** by Peggy O'Shea

ACROSS
1 2001 Dennis Hopper film
5 Sectors
10 RBI or ERA
14 Dies ___
15 Jog
16 Mannheim mister
17 Sequence
19 Sicilian resort
20 Snakebite drug
21 Once in a blue moon
23 Itsy-bitsy
24 Make a pumpkin face
25 Nobelist Egyptian
28 Gibber-jabbered
32 Pesky African fly
34 Great lake
35 Inscribed 56
36 Glorified gofer
37 Maria's brother in West Side Story
39 Move like a gull
40 Dictator Amin
41 Farming prefix
42 Titling
44 Awardee, e.g.
47 Close-grained
48 Hersey bell town
49 Omani coin
51 Be pensioned
53 St. John Lateran, for one
57 Melange
58 Kind of storm or tape
60 Allied group
61 Defiant type
62 California wine valley
63 Counting-out word
64 Stockholm citizen
65 Highland lowland

DOWN
1 Maggie Simpson's sister
2 Make ___ for it
3 NAFTA, for one
4 Destroy
5 Potsie portrayer Williams
6 Countryish
7 Brickell or Adams
8 Have ___ at (try)
9 Surprise hit
10 Put on ice
11 Filet mignon
12 Pisa's waterway
13 Cable carrier?
18 Emends
22 "A Dream" artist
24 Part of a hand
25 One of a flight
26 Thespian's whisper
27 Teaching asset
29 Everglades bird
30 Chris in Captain America
31 Solemn song
33 Train VIPs
38 Mars: Comb. form
39 Nosy activity?
41 Three-banded armadillo
43 "Robin ___" (old ballad)
45 Stupidity
46 Tracked down
50 Carpet fiber
51 Boxer's ringside wrap
52 Glamour competitor
53 Tony winner Neuwirth
54 Suffix for angel
55 Superman's wear
56 Cumming in Burlesque
59 Muppet Zealand

★★ Sudoku Twin

Fill in the grid so that each row, each column and each 3 x 3 frame contains every number from 1 to 9. A sudoku twin is two connected 9 x 9 sudokus.

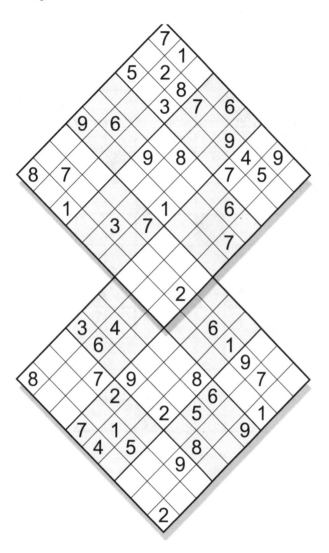

CHANGE ONE

Change one letter in each of these two words to form a common two-word phrase. There may be more than one possible answer.

ROUBLE RAKE

★★★ Futoshiki

Fill in the 5 x 5 grid with the numbers from 1 to 5 once per row and column, while following the greater than/lesser than symbols shown. There is only one valid solution that can be reached through logic and clear thinking alone!

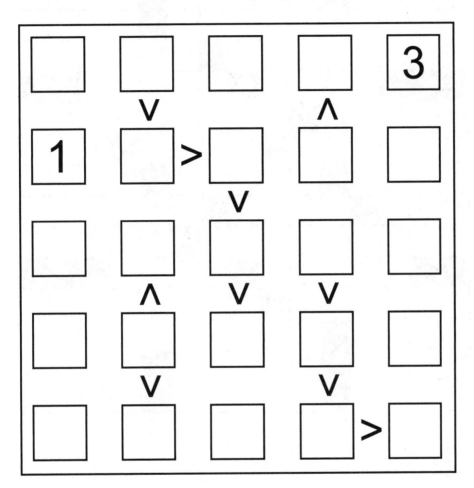

SANDWICH

What five-letter word belongs between the word at left and the word at right, so that the first and second word, and the second and third word, each form a common compound word or phrase?

CROSS _ _ _ _ _ POINT

★★★★ Mixed Bag by Peggy O'Shea

ACROSS

1 Variety of pea
5 Rower's craft
10 Help a weightlifter
14 Hawaiian city
15 "Someday" singer Mariah
16 Honduras port
17 Esteem
19 Part of QED
20 Horse operas
21 "White ___ of Dover"
23 Virginia willow
24 Did superbly
25 Stevens in *Hang 'em High*
28 Schnoz
32 Heartbreak
34 Make ___ for it
35 Explosive letters
36 Aphrodite's love
37 Ed in *Elf*
39 Location
40 "I ___ woodland fellow ...": Shak.
41 Bed piece
42 Abounding
44 Flood
47 Last test
48 What secrets are kept under
49 Frequently
51 Protector of Odysseus
53 Uproar
57 Minnow, often
58 Perks
60 Yours and mine
61 Moray trapper
62 Bring in from the fields
63 On the Adriatic
64 Esther in *Driving Miss Daisy*
65 Grounded jets

DOWN

1 *Candida* playwright
2 Pheasant's brood
3 Handouts to the poor
4 Battle of Tours locale
5 Frighten
6 Short snooze
7 *Exodus* novelist Leon
8 Zodiac sign
9 City of central Virginia
10 Beer mugs
11 Ideal quality
12 *Lemony Snicket* villain
13 Makes lace
18 Pleasantly dated
22 Canadian dollar bird
24 Tender
25 Violinist Stern
26 Talmadge of the silents
27 *Jaws* shark
29 Sounds off
30 Prefix before mural or state
31 *Loving* author Danielle
33 Desktop background
38 Gives a quote
39 Snakes along
41 Read the UPC
43 Run ___ of the law
45 "Queen of Soul" Franklin
46 Phenomenon
50 Anjou valley
51 "Name of the Game" group
52 New Mexico art colony
53 Paxton or Clinton
54 Many, many years
55 Race prelim
56 Horned snakes
59 Antique auto

★ BrainSnack®—Color Me Up

Which square (1–14) is colored incorrectly?

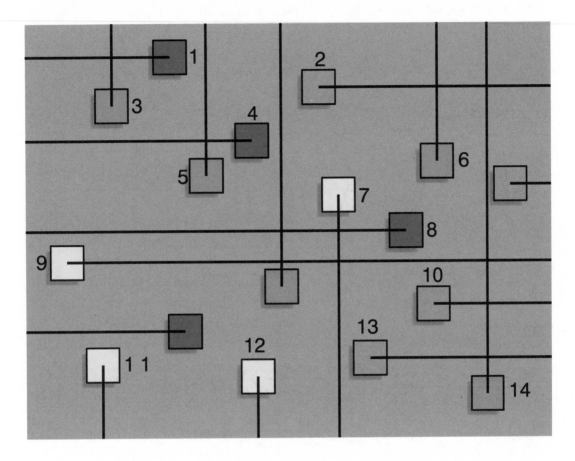

CONNECT TWO

An oxymoron is a combination of seemingly contradictory or incongruous words, such as "Science Fiction" (Science means "knowledge or study dealing with facts or truth" while Fiction means "an imagined or invented creation"). Connect the words with meanings that oppose each other and make oxymorons.

NEW	DONE
ALMOST	IMPROVED
GRADUATE	STRANGERS
INTIMATE	STUDENT

★ Concentration—Translation

Here are the Chinese numbers 1 through 10 and the numbers 52 and 13. Based on this information, translate the numbers above to Chinese and the Chinese numbers to western (Arabic) numerals.

1	2	3	4	5
一	二	三	四	五

6	7	8	9	10
六	七	八	九	十

52 → 五十二	十三 → 13
60 →	十一 →
76 →	三十八 →
99 →	五十八 →

UNCANNY TURN

Rearrange the letters of the word below to form a cognate anagram, one which is related or connected in meaning to the original phrase. The answer can be one or more words.

FACES ONE AT THE END

★★★★ Sci-Fi Writers by John M. Samson

ACROSS

1 Spanish appetizers
6 "Flying Scotsman" Liddell
10 Intellect
14 Standing straight
15 Godfather in *The Godfather*
16 Sailing
17 *Ringworld* author
19 Like sourballs
20 Hirsch in *Alpha Dog*
21 Verbal assault
23 Dire situations
26 Like boot-camp training
27 Bitter oranges
28 Corkscrew
29 Dada cofounder
32 "Indubitably!"
33 Lake Geneva feeder
34 Wait partner
35 Pen points
36 Throws stones at
37 Archaeological spots
38 Abbr. at Heathrow
39 Tramps
40 Pay a bill
41 *Come ___?* (Italian greeting)
42 Three-sided sword
43 Morph into
44 Baseless column
46 Idle chatter
47 James in *Our Man Flint* star
49 Malodorous
50 Six-foot birds
51 *The Mysterious Island* author
56 Classify
57 Right away!
58 Become hardened to
59 North Pole products
60 Baked veggies
61 Make off with

DOWN

1 ___ Aviv
2 Heavenly altar
3 Part of RPM
4 Land figures
5 Confounds
6 Wicked ways
7 Bank of Paris
8 Suffix for Gotham
9 Comprises
10 Motherly prefix
11 *I, Robot* author
12 Dweeb
13 Oasis fruit
18 Little lice
22 Castaway's home
23 Part of 57 Across
24 Concert souvenir
25 *The Martian Chronicles* author
26 *Puss in ___* (2011)

28 Lover of Daphnis
30 Ruling government
31 Pick on
33 Medieval bow instrument
36 Fop
37 Self-indulgent
39 "Mein ___" (*Cabaret* song)
40 Experiences déjà vu
43 Faces the pitcher
45 Topples from power
46 Marshmallow chicks
47 ___ *la vie!*
48 1847 South Seas tale
49 Ruse
52 "God Bless the ___": Greenwood
53 Feel remorse
54 "Right to bear arms" org.
55 Scaleless fish

★★ Keep Going

Start on a blank square of your choice and connect as many blank squares as possible with one single continuous line. You can only connect squares along vertical and horizontal lines, not along diagonal lines. You must continue the connecting line up until the next obstacle, i.e., the rim of the box, a black square or a square that has already been used. You can change direction at any obstacle you meet. Each square can be used only once. The number of blank squares that will be left unused is marked in the upper square. There is more than one solution. We show only one solution.

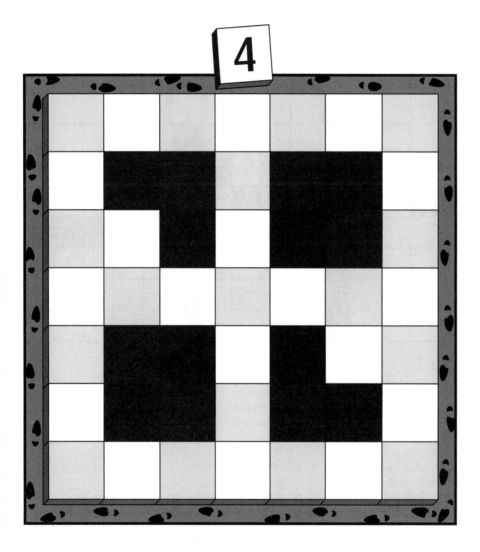

FRIENDS?

What do the following words have in common?

ACTIVE CHARGE EMOTIONAL INFLATION LINK MARKET

★ Wine

All the words are hidden vertically, horizontally or diagonally—in both directions. The letters that remain unused form a sentence from left to right.

```
R E T S I N A P L A B E L S S
H Y L R H O N E V A L L E Y U
C L E S O M L Y R R E H S R G
O H X T U A S N I C E P R A A
A D I O C S U R B M A L A H R
E S S A Z L E T O R O P G R S
Y E D H N S P A R K L I N G G
M E R L O T U N D D R N I E D
S O A M P F I V E I N O L S C
Y E L L A V A P A N E T S Y A
T A C A U L B R U D S A E I B
A N O J I E B O X U L G I R E
N O H O L P E E T G O E R T R
N N O I L L Y A C T M A I E N
I K L R A R I C A N L H G R E
N A R P C E V I N L W E E S T
W E R O E A R I E D A M R E S
I S T A C N T C U L I N A R Y
```

ELZAS
GLASS
GRAPE
LABEL
LAMBRUSCO
MADEIRA
MALBEC
MERLOT
MOSEL
NAPA VALLEY
PAUILLAC
PINOTAGE
RETSINA
RHONE VALLEY
RIESLING
RIOJA
SHERRY
SPARKLING
SUGARS
SYRAH
TANNIN
WHITE

ALCOHOL   CABERNET   CINSAUT
BORDEAUX   CELLAR   CORK
BOTTLE   CHIANTI   CULINARY

LETTERBLOCKS

Move the letterblocks around so that words are formed on top and below that you can associate with emotions.

★★★★ Movie Villains by John M. Samson

ACROSS

1 Price-tag info
5 Dressed to the ___
10 Sixth-day creation
14 Madonna's circle
15 Immobile
16 Hollow between hills
17 Powerful mite
18 Whooping bird
19 Country statistic
20 *The Dark Knight* villain
22 Like most greenhouse plants
24 Coleridge's "France: An ___"
25 Team cheer
26 *Show Boat* heroine
31 Passion
34 Bahrain bigwig
35 Rx offerings
37 Sky altar
38 Goes for the gold?
39 Tip the scales
40 Correct texts
41 Equivocate
42 Atelier sight
43 Winter precip
44 All eyes
46 Sororal
48 Draft pick?
49 Intention
50 Faith
53 *Batman and Robin* villain
58 Bring the house down
59 Emanations
61 Noncoms
62 Chess great Nimzovich
63 Hägar the Horrible's dog
64 Harness gait
65 Brings a halt to
66 Present
67 Tokyo sport

DOWN

1 Shoot the breeze
2 Imprecation
3 Type of gin
4 Henry Fielding novel
5 Quarter fifth
6 About, in contracts
7 Imminent
8 Seagoing raptor
9 Footprint
10 2009 James Cameron film
11 *Star Wars* villain
12 Safe from the storm
13 Beowulf's beverage
21 Food quality
23 Rock group
26 Bowling-pin wood
27 At great speed
28 *Superman II* villain
29 *The ___ of March* (2011)
30 Zodiac ram
31 Alphabetic sequence
32 This window stands out
33 Worn and torn
36 Not a pretty-sounding fruit
39 Peasant rebel Tyler
40 Fire and water, e.g.
42 Fencing sword
43 Jail, to a hood
45 *War of the Worlds* villains
47 Type of pin
50 Highlands hillside
51 Be a breadwinner
52 Some greens play this way
53 TV palomino
54 ___ avis (one of a kind)
55 Neutral shade
56 Closeup lens
57 This, in España
60 Game with "Draw Two" cards

★★★ Sport Maze

Draw the shortest way from the ball to the goal. You can only move along vertical and horizontal lines, not along diagonal lines. The figure on each square indicates the number of squares the ball must be moved in the same direction. You can change direction at each stop.

4	4	5	3	5	4
5	3	1	4	3	1
2	1	0	3	3	
2	4	1	2	2	3
5	2	2	2	1	1
2	1	1	5	1	1

DOUBLETALK

Homophones are words that share the same pronunciation, no matter how they are spelled. If they are spelled differently then they are called heterographs. Find heterographs meaning:

MUSICAL NOTE and LIGHT ROPE

★★★★ Classic Cinema by Tim Wagner

ACROSS

1 Place to drop anchor
5 One of Israel's 12 tribes
10 Crinkly cabbage
14 Takeoff specialist
15 "Higher Love" singer Winwood
16 He had an "Irish Rose"
17 Japanese Peace Nobelist
18 Bentley radials
19 Greenish blue
20 *Horse Feathers* stars
23 Bikini top
24 Mystifier Geller
25 Sound-alike word
29 Slave's dream
33 Heavenly prefix
34 Put in office
36 Campus in Troy, NY
37 "Don't just stand there!"
38 Bluish gray
39 2007 Nelly Furtado hit
40 Suffix with opal
41 Drink with foam
42 Sierra ___
43 Brayers
45 More petite
47 *Cómo es ___?* ("Why?")
48 Jackie's magnate
49 *Marathon Man* star
58 Bring down
59 "___ Day's Night": Beatles
60 In addition
61 Language that gave us whiskey
62 Street carnival
63 Hayworth in *Gilda*
64 Flippered animal
65 Williams of *Happy Days*
66 One Earth orbit

DOWN

1 *Remembrance of Things ___*: Proust
2 Oval-shaped fish
3 Nerve network
4 Glenn Miller's instrument
5 Off course
6 Hades river
7 Saffron, e.g.
8 "... happily ___ after"
9 Asset
10 Olsen or Lee Gifford
11 Have ___ in one's bonnet
12 Makeup artist?
13 Slithery fishes
21 River in Florence
22 Transport allowance
25 Like a rainforest
26 University of Maine site
27 Acknowledged expert
28 How Frosty disappears
29 Lavish celebrations
30 Slaver
31 Get off one's chest
32 Picture frame corner
35 Back muscle
38 "Toodle-oo" in Tokyo
39 Focus of a UPS tracking
41 ___ majesté
42 "That's My Baby" singer White
44 Ear component
46 Karl in *Patton*
49 Dregs
50 Interlaken river
51 *Superman II* villainess
52 Jackie in "Shanghai Noon"
53 Vase handles
54 Cookies 'n Cream cookie
55 "Would ___ to You?": Eurythmics
56 *Se Me ___ Escapando*: ABBA
57 Back end

1	2	3	4		5	6	7	8	9		10	11	12	13
14					15						16			
17					18						19			
20				21						22				
			23						24					
25	26	27				28		29				30	31	32
33					34	35					36			
37				38						39				
40				41						42				
43			44				45	46						
			47					48						
49	50	51			52	53	54				55	56	57	
58				59						60				
61				62						63				
64				65						66				

★ Spot the Differences

Find the nine differences in the image on the right.

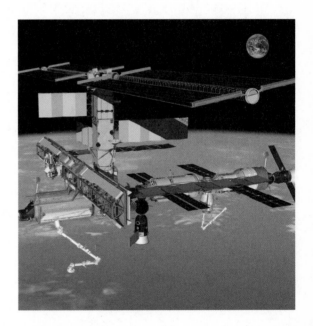

BLOCK ANAGRAM

Form the word that is described in the brackets with the letters above the grid. Extra letters are already in the right place.

INNOCENT (large assembly)

			V				O	

★★★ Sudoku

Fill in the grid so that each row, each column and each 3 x 3 frame contains every number from 1 to 9.

		7			2			
	3							
		9				8		6
							9	
			4	8				5
	6					3		
			9		7			8
	7			3		4	6	
1				6	8		2	3

ONE LETTER LESS OR MORE

The word on the right side contains the letters of the word on the left side plus or minus the letter in the middle. One letter is already in the right place.

C A N A R I E S +M A ☐ ☐ ☐ ☐ ☐ ☐ ☐

★★ Word Sudoku

Complete the grid so that each row, each column and each 3 x 3 frame contains the nine letters from the black box below. The hidden nine-letter word is in the diagonal from top left to bottom right.

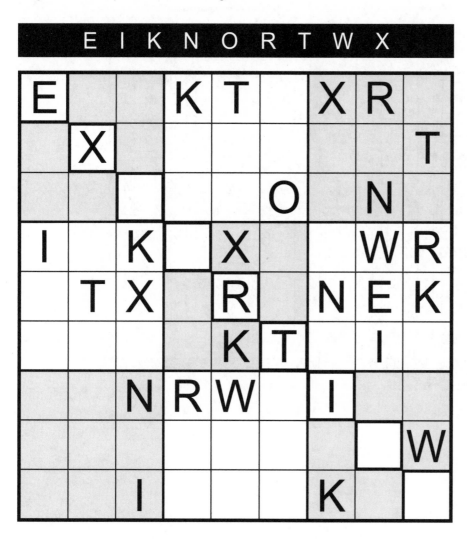

E I K N O R T W X

DOODLE PUZZLE

A doodle puzzle is a combination of images, letters and/or numbers that represent a word or a concept. If you cannot solve a doodle puzzle, do not look at the answer right away. Think hard—and outside the box.

DES
DES

★★★ BrainSnack®—Mirror, Mirror

Frame B is the horizontal mirror image of A. Which opening (1–8) is drawn incorrectly?

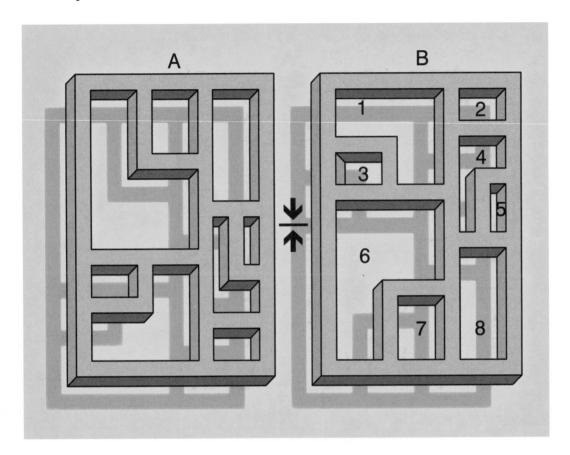

END GAME

The words you are seeking all have the letters END in them in the position indicated.
When you have found all of the answers from the clues on the right, one column will reveal the END GAME word which is believable.

_ E N D _ _ _	Connective tissue
_ E N D _ _ _	Presents for consideration
_ _ E N D _ _	Lacking a conclusion
_ _ _ E N D _	Lengthens

★★★★ Antonyms by Linda Lather

ACROSS

1 Nick and Nora's pet
5 Cry*
10 1978 Len Deighton novel
14 Guzzling sound
15 Listless feeling
16 Collective abbr.
17 Mechanical memorization
18 Coming*
19 Singer India.___
20 Scarce*
22 Forerunner
24 Portable place to sleep
25 Luau souvenir
26 Mentors*
31 Stirred
34 Heats
35 Carnival barker's delivery
37 Medicare choice
38 Rainbows
39 Piquant
40 Whole ball of wax
41 Finback whale
42 *Finnegans Wake* author
43 Mount Ida's island
44 Maze borders
46 Given, as a post
48 Hesitant sounds
49 First Burmese premier
50 Precepts
53 Forget*
58 Feed the kitty
59 Skyscraper girder
61 ___ *Enchanted* (2004)
62 Frog relative
63 Far from tight
64 In apple pie order
65 Friend by treaty
66 Winner*
67 Adjust the Steinway

DOWN

1 Taj Mahal site
2 No neatnik
3 Outfit for Pavlova
4 Federal bodies
5 Vatican representative
6 Shortly, poetically
7 Company or regiment
8 Squirt ___
9 Expensive
10 Charred the surface of
11 Bend*
12 *Hillary's Choice* author Sheehy
13 Drained of resources
21 Syndicate heads
23 End of the Jewish calendar
26 Curbside pile
27 Sidewalk show
28 Planned*

29 Catch sight of
30 Virgo's alpha star
31 Ottoman governor
32 Theatricalize
33 Visited slumberland
36 Seals, slangily
39 Distress call
40 War of words
42 Amusing act
43 French film
45 Piggish
47 Winter*
50 Toodle-oo
51 Organic compound
52 Window ledge
53 Antique autos
54 Make bearable
55 ___ cheese dressing
56 Distinctive flair
57 Have status
60 Ghost's cry

★ Hourglass

Starting in the middle, each word in the top half has the letters of the word below it, plus a new letter, and each word in the bottom half has the letters of the word above it, plus a new letter.

(1) destructive sea wave
(2) State capital of Texas
(3) sisters of your father or mother
(4) warm-water fatty fish
(5) change direction
(6) ruined by overcooking
(7) pitcher that hits
(8) protector, elected official in the Roman Republic

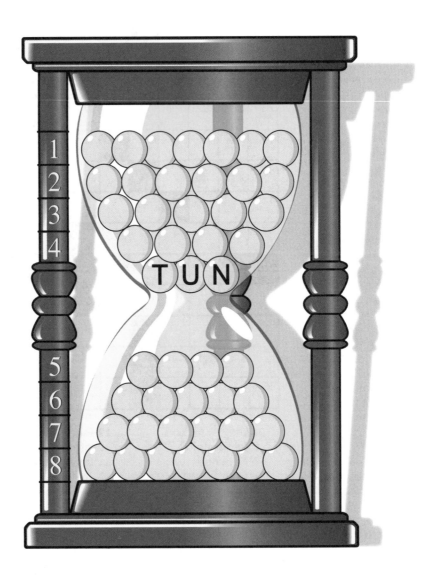

MISSING LETTER MOTTO

Fill in each missing letter, indicated by an X, to make a well-known motto.

XRUTX AXX XIXTXE

★ Horoscope

Fill in the grid so that every row, every column and every frame of six boxes contains six different symbols: health, work, money, happiness, family and love. Look at the row or column that corresponds with your sign of the zodiac and find out which of the six symbols are important for you today. The symbols appear in increasing order of importance (1–6). It's up to you to translate the meaning of each symbol to your specific situation.

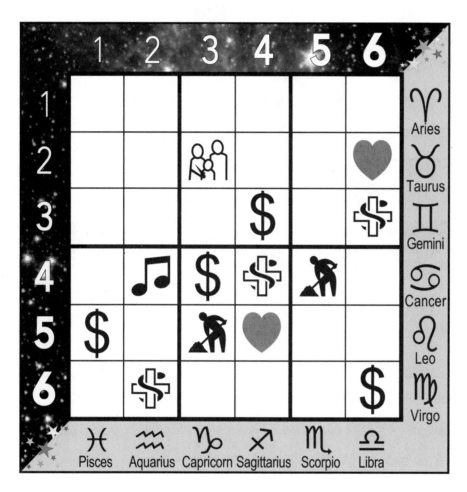

END GAME

The words you are seeking all have the letters END in them in the position indicated. When you have found all of the answers, from the clues on the right, one column will reveal the END GAME word which is really annoying.

_	_	_	_	E	N	D		Make believe
_	_	_	E	N	D	_		Uses up
_	_	E	N	D	_	_		Thin
_	E	N	D	_	_	_		Offers

★★★★ Mishmash by Peggy O'Shea

ACROSS

1 Poi root
5 *Ivanhoe* author
10 Pitchfork-shaped letters
14 Kuwait resident
15 Dried coconut
16 Enjoy a charter boat
17 Ursa Minor
19 Rod in a hot rod
20 South African capital
21 *The Caretaker* playwright
23 Infamous marquis
24 High-priced spread?
25 Bolo tie feature
28 P.C. Wren novel
32 Make atonement for
34 Kedrova in *Zorba the Greek*
35 Ending for pamphlet
36 Footless animal
37 Tabriz resident
39 Tolstoy heroine Karenina
40 Gibson in *The Beaver*
41 Tiny insect
42 Bangs, yells, sirens, etc.
44 Blocked
47 Rock climber's ridge
48 Web spots
49 College drill team
51 One may be called in court
53 Nonconformist
57 Place for a timer
58 In the first place
60 Ireland's ___ Féin
61 Eagle's grasper
62 Poke around
63 Resort north of Provo
64 Unaccompanied
65 Lacking thrills

DOWN

1 1, on the Mohs scale
2 Zone
3 Speak harshly
4 Like stalkers
5 Cape Cod fish
6 Fly trap
7 Dentist's word
8 "___-la-la": Gershwin
9 Infield cover
10 Show horses do this
11 Remote viewing, for one
12 At a standstill
13 Psychic
18 Troop encampment
22 Young Frankenstein's wife
24 Kind of forest
25 Marathoner's woe
26 Social outcast
27 Youthful
29 Cheer up
30 Conviction
31 Render unreadable
33 North Star State
38 Charlie Brown's expletive
39 Lockheed Martin products
41 Groks
43 Like Lucky Charms
45 *The Third Man* setting
46 *How to Train Your ___* (2010)
50 Like Bo Peep's charges
51 Edwin Drood's fiancée
52 Wicked
53 Minderbinder of *Catch-22*
54 Intestine divisions
55 Skelton's bumpkin
56 NFL QB Orton
59 "Too-Ra-Loo-Ra-Loo-___"

★ Energy

All the words are hidden vertically, horizontally or diagonally—in both directions. The letters that remain unused form a sentence from left to right.

```
R O T A R E N E G A C W C O R
D B I N G P L U T O N I U M T
O T I H E S L E C A W N O F C
N S O O T O M N U L S D E R V
A O T N M L I O O F E F N T O
F F T S I A E C T E N A U E R
G R S W Y E S S L A T R R T H
E A U T E O T S E I B M N T A
M L A T M N O S U I M E N P T
U C O M P O S T N O D A F O E
I H N E C I T E N I K G T W C
N E R G E Y I N C A E N N E O
A R I L S O L C S A T I E R A
R N U D S Y A S T T E M M R L
U O V E N E H M T H E R M A L
J B A I N E S S C I M A N Y D
C Y O N A S T A N T O W M V E
R L T T C I T E N G A M I M E
```

EINSTEIN
FUEL
GENERATOR
HEAT
JOULE
KINETIC
MAGNETIC
MASS
NEWTON
NUCLEAR
OVEN
PLUTONIUM
POWER
SOOT
STEAM
THERMAL
TURBINE
TURF
URANIUM
WARMING
WIND FARM

ACCIDENT
ATOMS
BIOMASS

CHERNOBYL
CLIMATE
COAL

COMPOST
DIESEL
DYNAMICS

UNCANNY TURN

Rearrange the letters of the word below to form a cognate anagram, one which is related or connected in meaning to the original phrase. The answer can be one or more words.

HER TOP NOISES RANG

★★★ Binairo

Complete the grid with zeros and ones until there are 5 zeros and 6 ones in every row and every column. No more than two of the same number can be next to or under each other. Rows or columns with exactly the same content are not allowed. There is only one valid solution.

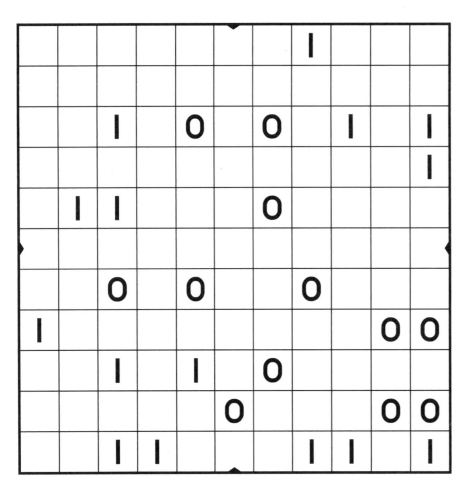

DOUBLETALK

Homophones are words that share the same pronunciation, no matter how they are spelled. If they are spelled differently then they are called heterographs. Find heterographs meaning:

FAILED TO HIT and FOG

★★★★ La Scala Title Roles by Linda Lather

ACROSS

1 Make a trade
5 ___ *Blues* (Taj Mahal album)
10 Blanchett in *Oscar and Lucinda*
14 Seed jacket
15 Rage on stage
16 Hale of *Gilligan's Island*
17 Cio-Cio San
20 Sample for the lab
21 Andes grazer
22 Summarily let go
23 Onion rings, e.g.
24 Averred
27 TV fundraiser
31 Hankerings
32 Pirate
33 Golfer's thrill
34 Tear apart
35 Pickled bud
36 Ticket
37 Abbr. on a road map
38 "The Thinker" sculptor
39 Renowned
40 Latino
42 Funny business
43 Place to play old records
44 Opera singer Haugland
45 Piece for a coloratura
48 *M*A*S*H* star?
52 Figaro
54 Mine, in Montréal
55 Mushroom with a spongy cap
56 Glitzy light
57 Yemeni capital
58 Like dirty chimneys
59 Spanish cat

DOWN

1 Neill and Shepard
2 Paper a present
3 Nursing assistant
4 Appeased
5 Felt
6 Root firmly
7 Person, place, or thing
8 Baseball's "Little Giant"
9 Merchant
10 Aladdin's transport
11 ___ Romeo sports car
12 Scented powder
13 "Storms in Africa" singer
18 Socializes
19 Official in the church
23 Septet
24 Koran chapter
25 Fountain of Rome
26 *Despicable Me* girl
27 Subject matter
28 Port-au-Prince locale
29 Eightsome
30 In dire straits
32 Forearm bones
35 Goes with the flow
36 Envelopment
38 Up the ante
39 Israeli desert region
41 Irrational dread
42 Recently
44 Strong point
45 Arab garments
46 *The King and I* king
47 Luke Donald's club
48 Hairstyle that's picked
49 Intestinal sections
50 Position to fill
51 Caesar's Palace game
53 Pedometer reading

★★★ Sport Maze

Draw the shortest way from the ball to the goal. You can only move along vertical and horizontal lines, not along diagonal lines. The figure on each square indicates the number of squares the ball must be moved in the same direction. You can change direction at each stop.

5	3	5	4	3	1
2	1	(1)	4	0	4
2	2	3	2	3	4
1	4	1	2	1	4
5	4	1	3	2	5
1	5	2	5	3	○

LETTER LINE

Put a letter in each of the squares below to make a word which means "CONDUCTOR." These numbered clues refer to other words which can be made from the whole.

1 5 2 4 4 6 10 A POUCH; 6 3 2 1 5 6 4 MADE POSSIBLE; 5 6 7 10 3 6 4 WELL READ; 5 2 3 4 6 4 ARRIVED

1	2	3	4	5	6	7	8	9	10

★★★ Kakuro

Each number in a black area is the sum of the numbers that you have to enter in the next empty boxes. The empty boxes that make up the sum are called a run. The sum of the across run is written above the diagonal in the black area and the sum of the down run is written below the diagonal. Runs can only contain the numbers 1 through 9 and each number in a run can only be used once. The gray boxes only contain odd numbers and the white only even numbers.

LETTERBLOCKS

Move the letterblocks around so that words are formed on top and below that you can associate with the Internet.

★★★★ Here Comes the Judge by John M. Samson

ACROSS
1 Pitfall
5 California peak
11 Money player
14 Saint Patrick's land
15 Canvassed
16 MacBook ___
17 Judge Dredd portrayer
19 Einstein's hometown
20 Wobbles
21 De Gaulle Museum site
23 Bridge side
24 Scottish terrier
26 French poodle name
29 Comforters
32 2003 Shia LaBeouf film
33 Strident noise
34 Bowl-shaped pan
35 Inspired wonder
36 Josh or rib
37 "Help!" in France
38 ___ Marcos, Texas
39 Farm buildings
40 Herbivore's snack
41 Carried away
43 Lufthansa fleet
44 Gold purity measure
45 2011 FedEx Cup winner
46 Hairy goat feature
48 Mozart's birthplace
52 Kind of doll
53 *Caddyshack* judge
57 Green in *Casino Royale*
58 Tell by heart
59 "___ nice place to visit ..."
60 Cozy room
61 Appeared
62 Cradle grain

DOWN
1 Put out feelers
2 Cause agitation
3 Gross in *Tinseltown*
4 Became a pain in the neck
5 Far from abundant
6 "In the Bleak Midwinter" composer
7 Everybody
8 Highway sign
9 Super score
10 Sweet girl of song
11 Judge Roy Bean portrayer
12 Brooklet
13 *Coffee, Tea ___?* (1973)
18 "___ in Heaven": Clapton
22 Vex
24 Kind of reunion
25 River of Bern
26 Lunar stage
27 Des Moines native
28 Supreme Court justice
29 Lacking spice
30 "Five ___": The Doors
31 Comical sketches
33 Soft hat
36 Canadian singer MacLean
37 Scrooge player Sim
39 Margins
40 Blood part
42 Tarnish
43 Stopped the DVD player
45 ___ couture
46 Begat
47 Soffit locale
49 Marriage, e.g.
50 *Casablanca* heroine
51 "Yesterday!"
54 Rock legend Jerry ___ Lewis
55 Rocks in bars
56 That fellow

★★ BrainSnack®—Lost Cube

On what base (1–9) will you put the small cube?

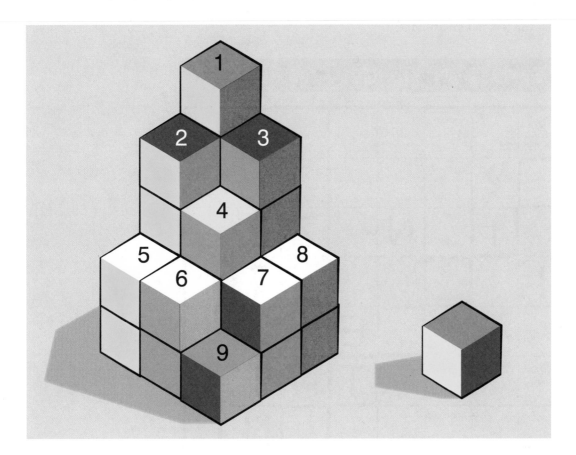

DOODLE PUZZLE

A doodle puzzle is a combination of images, letters and/or numbers that represent a word or a concept. If you cannot solve a doodle puzzle, do not look at the answer right away. Think hard—and outside the box.

★★★ Word Sudoku

Complete the grid so that each row, each column and each 3 x 3 frame contains the nine letters from the black box below. The hidden nine-letter word is in the diagonal from top left to bottom right.

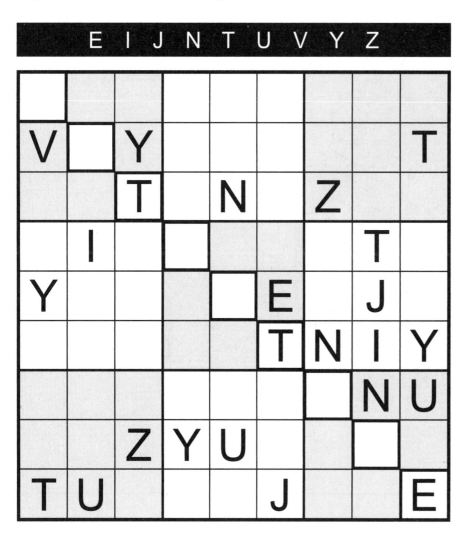

E I J N T U V Y Z

CHANGE ONE

Change one letter in each of these two words to form a common two-word phrase. There may be more than one possible answer.

GLUE GIBBON

★★★ BrainSnack®—Missing Number

Which number should replace the question mark?

END GAME

The words you are seeking all have the letters END in them in the position indicated.
When you have found all of the answers, from the clues on the right, one column will reveal the
END GAME word which could tie you up in knots.

| | | | E | N | D | | Contacts |
| _ | _ | _ | E | N | D | _ | Contacts |

_ _ _ E N D _ Contacts
_ _ _ _ E N D Unexpected and good
_ _ E N D _ _ One who pays
_ E N D _ _ _ Farewell party

★★★★ Themeless by Peggy O'Shea

ACROSS

1 Sugar cube
5 1988 Olympics host city
10 Ward in *Double Jeopardy*
14 Banned apple spray
15 Movie crowd member
16 Exciting experience, in slang
17 Unique devices
19 Icy coating
20 Tape container
21 Shards
23 Bacchanal cry
24 River through Interlaken
25 Dress with a flare
28 Blowout result
33 Catch sight of
35 "___ the torpedoes!": Farragut
36 Biochem strand
37 Parcel (out)
38 *Turandot* is one
40 Rain buckets
41 Wind direction
42 Gyrate
43 Loofa
45 Deceitful
48 Vicinities
49 Unrestrained revelry
50 In good health
52 Clans
55 Trustworthy
59 Make money
60 Gargantuan
62 Osaka sport
63 Quilt stuffing
64 "Don't count ___ !"
65 Generous slice
66 Henhouse "bed"
67 Dartle of *David Copperfield*

DOWN

1 Not religious
2 Forearm bone
3 Big D team
4 Bearing
5 Scuffle
6 Went off
7 Missouri River native
8 Banquet dispenser
9 Canary Islands seaport
10 Main drag
11 Stonestreet of *Modern Family*
12 Cuba libre ingredient
13 Primatology study
18 "Not on your life!"
22 Shah's domain, once
24 Ways away
25 Said some more
26 Téa in *Ghost Town*
27 New York team, familiarly
29 Spots of perfection
30 *Me, Myself & ___* (2000)
31 Europe's second largest lake
32 Roster listings
34 Stripling
39 Impala, to a lion
40 Bullfighter
42 Ran fast
44 *Going Rogue* author Sarah
46 Pal around
47 Topics of discourse
51 On one's toes
52 ___ *of the D'Urbervilles*
53 Ramirez of tennis
54 ___ *la Douce* (1963)
55 Take from square one
56 Bandmate of the Edge
57 *Belle de Jour* director Buñuel
58 *Cómo ___ usted?*
61 Home to Sugarloaf Mountain

★★★ Sudoku X

Fill in the grid so that each row, each column and each 3 x 3 frame contains every number from 1 to 9. The two main diagonals of the grid also contain every number from 1 to 9.

					6		2	
	1		5				9	
			1					3
	2	5	7	9				
		4						6
	4							
2	7			3		1	6	
		6		1		8		7

CHANGELINGS

Each of the three lines of letters below spell words which have a weaponry connection, but the letters have been mixed up. Four letters from the first word are now in the third line, four letters from the third word are in the second line and four letters from the second word are in the first line. The remaining letters are in their original places. What are the words?

S L K B A T I C O A
B U A C V B S T R D
A N I B E R A I L Y

★ Safe Code

To open the safe you have to replace the question mark with the correct figure. You can find this figure by determining the logical method behind the numbers shown. The methods may include calculation, inversion, repetition, chronological succession, or forming ascending and descending series.

SAFE A08

BLOCK ANAGRAM

Form the word that is described in the brackets with the letters above the grid. Extra letters are already in the right place.

PRINTED *(chief)*

			S		E		

★★★★★ Elementary School by John M. Samson

ACROSS

1 *Finding Nemo* shark
5 Sacred vocal composition
10 Cat's eye, sometimes
14 Coworker of Kent and Olsen
15 Athenian market
16 Tucker
17 Benchmark
19 Orchestra tuner
20 Stabilized
21 Chopin's country
23 Violinist Itzhak
24 Lust after
25 French body of water
26 Having star potential
29 Like a pixie
32 Curved sword
33 Rather than
34 Alaimo of *Star Trek: DS9*
35 Makes fun of
36 Frumpish
37 Water you can walk on
38 German pistol
39 "If I do ___ myself"
40 Deliverer
42 Blackout
43 ___ and drabs
44 Amazon River carnivore
48 Piece for a coloratura
50 They're left behind
51 Made a federal case out of it
52 Tonto's portrayer
54 Tennis champ Arthur
55 Cause of food poisoning
56 Wile E. Coyote's supplier
57 Ringtoss equipment
58 Stressed out
59 Insect home

DOWN

1 Hold fast
2 ___ cuisine
3 1994 Indy 500 winner
4 Like this puzzle's theme
5 Nut case
6 "The Centipede" poet Nash
7 Warty hopper
8 Bet on the wrong horse
9 Pollywogs
10 At a chop shop, perhaps
11 Replaceable pacemaker part
12 Golfer's choice
13 Off the grass, on the links
18 Clio Award winner
22 At an end
24 Highland Games pole
26 Gradually get narrow
27 Strife goddess
28 Test-drive car
29 Persian Gulf leader
30 Queen Anne's ___ (wild carrot)
31 Queen lead vocalist
32 Wise people
35 747, for one
36 Elixir-like
38 Island neckwear
39 Abraham's wife
41 Eats at the beach?
42 Heavyweight
44 Loud bursts
45 Family relation
46 Steering stations
47 Good looks or charm, e.g.
48 "Quick!"
49 Bit of subterfuge
50 French cathedral city
53 Score well on

★★ Keep Going

Start on a blank square of your choice and connect as many blank squares as possible with one single continuous line. You can only connect squares along vertical and horizontal lines, not along diagonal lines. You must continue the connecting line up until the next obstacle, i.e., the rim of the box, a black square or a square that has already been used. You can change direction at any obstacle you meet. Each square can be used only once. The number of blank squares that will be left unused is marked in the upper square. There is more than one solution. We show only one solution.

REPOSITION PREPOSITION

Unscramble FOR IN FONT and find a three-word preposition.

★ Word Ladder

Convert the word at the top of the ladder into the word at the bottom of it, using all the rungs in between. On each rung, you must put a valid word that has the same letters as the word above it, apart from one letter change. There may be more than one way of achieving this.

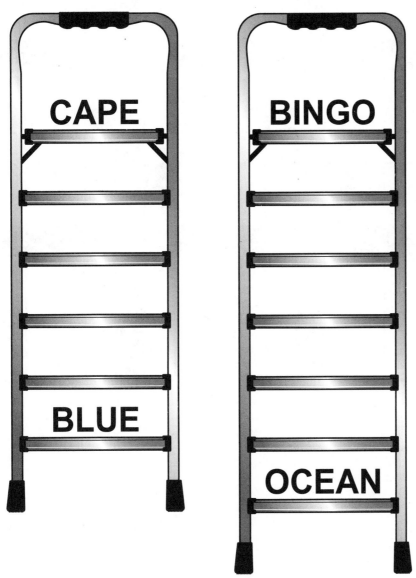

CAPE

BLUE

BINGO

OCEAN

DOUBLETALK

Homophones are words that share the same pronunciation, no matter how they are spelled. If they are spelled differently then they are called heterographs. Find heterographs meaning:

STAY and HOW HEAVY

★★★★★ Latin 101 by Tim Wagner

ACROSS

1 Sgt. Friday's org.
5 Legal paper
10 Table insert
14 Morales in *Paid in Full*
15 Back-bending dance
16 Hebrew month
17 Stipulation on some sales
18 Japanese seaport
19 Trident part
20 Unwelcome
23 Suffix with meteor
24 ___ Lung in *Kung Fu Panda*
25 Clinton or Handler
29 Seven-time Wimbledon winner
33 Part of AWOL
34 Unbind
36 Poetic preposition
37 Land of Dublin
38 Bejewel
39 In la-la land
40 Chemical suffix
41 Suspect's "out"
42 *The Vampire Diaries* heroine
43 1988 Schwarzenegger film
45 Violet variety
47 Slip up
48 90° from SSE
49 Not all there
58 Haywire
59 Met soprano Tokody
60 Overly contrived
61 India.Arie music
62 Land of Sherpas
63 Juvenile
64 Whet
65 Quebec peninsula
66 Cullen family matriarch

DOWN

1 Hurdle
2 Düsseldorf donkey
3 Duo
4 Melt
5 Flaxen-haired
6 Lovely Beatles girl
7 Bowie's model wife
8 River of Spain
9 Place for a coin toss
10 Pull out all stops
11 "Ellistoniana" essayist
12 "Go tell ___ Rhody ..."
13 Wingless parasite
21 River of Picardy
22 "Candy Land" is one
25 Crystalline
26 "Atta Troll" poet Heinrich
27 Like little pitchers?
28 Taxing ordeal?
29 Muscle-fiber furrow
30 Middle Ages fiddle
31 The Palestra, e.g.
32 Car for a family of four
35 Social bigwig, in British slang
38 Frightful
39 Estrange
41 Prefix with dynamic
42 Bald eagle relative
44 Annoy a comedian
46 Like LPGA members
49 Humorist Ogden
50 1847 South Seas adventure
51 It takes a verb
52 "Spare me," for one
53 "Sorry about that!"
54 Lose one's cool
55 "___ bien!"
56 Tabloid twosome
57 "Same Old Lang ___": Fogelberg

★ BrainSnack®—Pricey Painting

How much does the last painting cost?

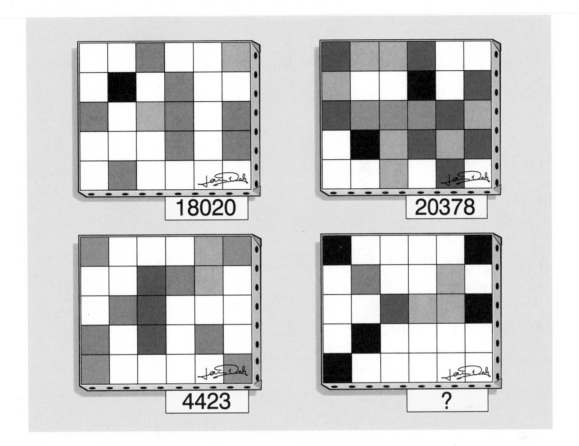

18020

20378

4423

?

DOODLE PUZZLE

A doodle puzzle is a combination of images, letters and/or numbers that represent a word or a concept. If you cannot solve a doodle puzzle, do not look at the answer right away. Think hard—and outside the box.

★ Word Wheel

How many words of three or more letters, each including the letter at the center of the wheel, can you make from this diagram? No plurals or conjugations. We found 18, including one nine-letter word. Can you do better?

UNCANNY TURN

Rearrange the letters of the word below to form a cognate anagram, one which is related or connected in meaning to the original phrase. The answer can be one or more words.

DUE CROP

★★★★★ Melange by Karen Peterson

ACROSS

1 ___ plaisir!
5 Ringing sound
10 Pewter component
14 A tribe of Israel
15 Cliff hanger?
16 Bushy hairdo
17 Linda in *Liberty Stands Still*
19 Warp-drive vehicles
20 Amusing icebreaker
21 San ___ (Apennines republic)
23 Sediment
24 Minstrel's instrument
25 Washbowls
28 Plant scientist
31 Bates and Hale
32 "Light My Fire" group
33 Greek letter
34 Performed an aria
35 Wingding
36 Little annoyance
37 "Thank God ___ Country Boy"
38 Character builders?
39 Formal fiats
40 Admitted defeat
42 Orison
43 *The Canterbury ___*
44 Weaver's device
45 Paddock sounds
47 Saved from ruin
51 Nomadic shelter
52 Whistle-blower
54 Lake near Niagara Falls
55 Banded marble
56 Triplet
57 Hard up
58 Sophia in *El Cid*
59 "A likely story!"

DOWN

1 "A" in code
2 Jugular, for one
3 Bacchanal "whoopee!"
4 In a holding pattern
5 They're paddled, but not spanked
6 Riga residents
7 "I Am Not My Hair" singer
8 *Little Birds* author Anaïs
9 High school math
10 Bacall in *Key Largo*
11 Apartment with kitchen
12 *East of Eden* brother
13 "I can only ___ much"
18 Paradises
22 Arab garments
24 Alex Haley book
25 No-frills
26 Landmark in 27 Down
27 Texas city
28 Far from interested
29 Condition
30 Siberian people
32 Claire in *Les Misérables*
35 Statue base
36 Paul in *The Ides of March*
38 Do-re-mi
39 Teed off
41 2002 Peace Nobelist
42 Allergy cause
44 Starbucks order
45 Make a move
46 Wolfe in *Fer-de-Lance*
47 Magi guide
48 Clothes
49 Nobelist Wiesel
50 Fender flaw
53 Back from now

★★★ Sport Maze

Draw the shortest way from the ball to the goal. You can only move along vertical and horizontal lines, not along diagonal lines. The figure on each square indicates the number of squares the ball must be moved in the same direction. You can change direction at each stop.

2	1	5	4	5	4
2	0	4	1	1	1
2	4	1	2	2	3
2	2	2	3	4	1
1		3	1	2	1
2	3	2	5	1	2

DELETE ONE

Delete one letter from LADIES and make perfect.

★★★ Word Sudoku

Complete the grid so that each row, each column and each 3 x 3 frame contains the nine letters from the black box below. The hidden nine-letter word is in the diagonal from top left to bottom right.

A C E L M N P R W

	P					N	A	
R		E		M			C	
		L		A	N			
	M				E			W
		R						
			M	A	E			L
				R			W	
L								
P		W						R

ONE LETTER LESS OR MORE

The word on the right side contains the letters of the word on the left side plus or minus the letter in the middle. One letter is already in the right place.

E A R N I N G S ⊕W **A** ☐ ☐ ☐ ☐ ☐ ☐ ☐

★ Spot the Differences

Find the nine differences in the image on the right.

FRIENDS?

What do the following words have in common?

ABSENTEE CRITIC ANTIQUARIAN VOODOO REPUBLICAN

★★★★★ Variety Pack by Maggie Ellis

ACROSS

1 Capital on the Aare
5 Netherworld
10 Spreadsheet filler
14 Jai ___
15 Bakery lure
16 Joie de vivre
17 Excalibur's owner
19 Guitar adjunct
20 Rolle and Williams
21 Really dry
23 Prefix for cycle
24 ___ de guerre
25 On target
29 Customized
33 "Another Pyramid" musical
34 Helicopter blade
36 Medical insurance plan
37 "Send in the Clowns" composer
41 Hours in a Jupiter day
42 Williams of *Happy Days*
43 Kenton or Stanley Gardner
44 ___ and battery
46 Daily specials
49 Harper Valley org.
50 "Tic-tac-toe" winner
51 Evening service
55 Least possible
59 Beyond bad
60 *Forrest Gump* star
62 Surrealist Magritte
63 Harden
64 Zeno of ___
65 Michaels of Poison
66 Cézanne contemporary
67 Do a washday chore

DOWN

1 Pop in the oven
2 New Haven students
3 Dennis Miller specialty
4 Snort before bedtime
5 ___ Tweed
6 Techniques
7 Word spoken with a head slap
8 Tall birds
9 Susan in *Thelma & Louise*
10 Aide-___
11 Having wings
12 Madrid appetizer
13 In good time
18 Gas prefix
22 What misers do
25 Rotini or orzo
26 Baptism et al.
27 Delightful places
28 "Forest and Dove" painter Max
29 Set things right
30 Cry of accomplishment
31 De Becque in *South Pacific*
32 Biospheres
35 Spanish bear
38 ___ cuisine
39 Blown up
40 Roles for leading ladies
45 Droid download
47 Bump and thump
48 Collette in *Little Miss Sunshine*
51 Win, lose or draw
52 "Did you ___?"
53 Trig function
54 Logical
55 Dyan's *Deathtrap* role
56 Perrier in *Murder by Death*
57 One logged on
58 Ravioli filling
61 Toupee, in slang

★★ BrainSnack®—Tick Tock

Which clock (A-E) shows the correct time in the afternoon knowing that two clocks are two hours wrong and the other two are running fast in the afternoon?

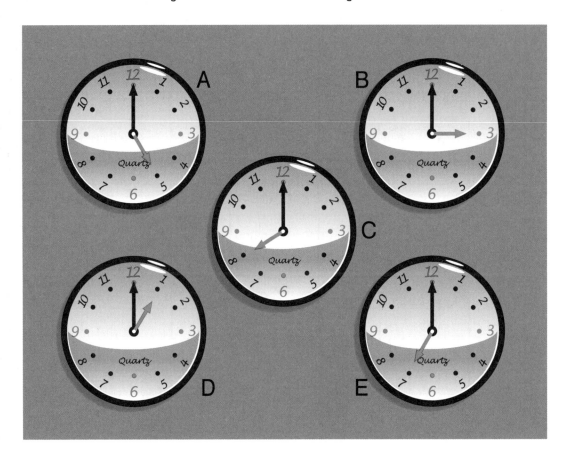

CHANGE ONE

Change one letter in each of these two words to form a common two-word phrase. There may be more than one possible answer.

CATCH OUR

★ Basketball

All the words are hidden vertically, horizontally or diagonally—in both directions. The letters that remain unused form a sentence from left to right.

```
T K H E N A C T I O N A L B A
T C S K E J O H N S O N T B D
E O B A C K B O A R D A L R L
K L A S C O R E S R C O A C H
S C R S S O C I A A G U T I O
A T O I T N O W E R G E N B A
B O D S O B R E N D L I N E S
F H M T O O D R I B B L E O P
M S A A F U R E L S N L H O O
R A N T T N I V L S A T O H R
B E E M O C O O U S D L F C T
T U P T V E H N O R R L F E K
P S C T I I G R F I O A E O U
U S B K P C O U R T J B N A S
Y K S T E A L T L A H P S A E
A T B A L T L C O M P M I E T
L T I T I O N I N T H U V I E
W O R B A C K D O O R J E L D
```

COACH
COURT
DRIBBLE
END LINE
FORWARD
FOUL LINE
GUARD
JOHNSON
JORDAN
JUMP BALL
LAY-UP
MATCH
OFFENSIVE
PIVOT FOOT
RODMAN
SCORE
SHOT CLOCK
SPORT
STEAL
TEAM
TIE
TURNOVER

ASPHALT   BACKDOOR   BOUNCE
ASSIST   BASKET   BUCKET
BACKBOARD   BLOCK   CHARGE

LETTERBLOCKS

Move the letterblocks around so that words are formed on top and below that you can associate with travel.

★★★★★ Themeless by John M. Samson

ACROSS

1 Cheese served in Athens
5 Writer's cramp, e.g.
10 Mosque prayer leader
14 Crowning
15 Eyelashes
16 Iditarod Trail end
17 Not quite a lead role
19 Gullible one
20 Gene in *Laura*
21 Effortless beyond compare
23 Keatsian poem
24 Turn one way
25 Seventh heaven
29 Sharp retort
33 "The Times They ___-Changin' ": Dylan
34 Game related to bingo
36 Mother goat
37 Small white dog
41 RSA political party
42 Mirage sights
43 Coldplay's "___ Love"
44 Iceberg ___
46 Blue
49 Prefix for corn
50 Pump
51 Settled a score
55 Twin sister of Apollo
59 Mortgage claim
60 Bobby's billy
62 Pond
63 Plunge into water
64 *The Time Machine* aristocrats
65 Wanted soldier
66 Camelot mail
67 Jalopy ding

DOWN

1 Observe Ramadan
2 Holder of notions
3 Drink like a fish
4 Blessing
5 Silk-___ painting
6 Condolence
7 Legendary boxing champ
8 Math curve
9 *O* or *GQ*
10 Rainbow color
11 Wry grimace
12 Rock-concert gear
13 Chance upon
18 Japanese skater Yoshie
22 Rich flavor
25 Like SpongeBob's voice
26 Peace goddess
27 Do a double take
28 Bring shame upon
29 *Midnight Cowboy* character
30 Left Bank river
31 Hobbit adolescent
32 Like a King novel
35 Scots uncle
38 "___ at Heart": Sinatra
39 Estate in España
40 Shot up
45 Carpal ___ syndrome
47 Swap
48 Retired fleet
51 *Brokeback Mountain* heroine
52 *A ___ to a Kill* (1985)
53 Architect Saarinen
54 Parisian fashion house
55 "I get it," humorously
56 Eight furlongs
57 Windows symbol
58 Comical sketch
61 Source of bubbles

1	2	3	4		5	6	7	8	9		10	11	12	13
14					15						16			
17			18								19			
20							21		22					
			23					24						
25	26	27				28		29				30	31	32
33						34	35					36		
37			38	39							40			
41				42							43			
44			45					46	47	48				
			49						50					
51	52	53				54		55				56	57	58
59					60		61							
62					63						64			
65					66						67			

★★★ BrainSnack®—The Sky's the Limit

Which skyscraper (1–5) has to turn one more light on?

DOODLE PUZZLE

A doodle puzzle is a combination of images, letters and/or numbers that represent a word or a concept. If you cannot solve a doodle puzzle, do not look at the answer right away. Think hard—and outside the box.

★ Illnesses

All the words are hidden vertically, horizontally or diagonally—in both directions. The letters that remain unused form a sentence from left to right.

```
H E A D A C H E C H P B J I L
D H O O I D F I L A L R A E N
C H R O N I C I R E S U U R S
H O P E R S N A S A R I N U A
O G L E E V S F T S I S D T M
L A A D H I B N L R U E I C O
E N G A T L A A D U I R C A L
R G U E I T S E C F E V E R U
A R E A S T S Y C T S N E F N
S E T I C H T H D A E T Z A A
R N S E H N R P A O O R T A R
U E S U E A O O L B B L I Y G
R S E R M I K R A O S I U A S
V A C C I N E T E B U C T T A
R F E V A M E A S L E S E N E
M A L A R I A R U Y C O N S A
P N E U M O N I A T A G I O S
U S H G U O C G N I P O O H W
```

FEVER
FISSURE
FLU
FRACTURE
GANGRENE
GRANULOMA
HEADACHE
HERNIA
INFLUENZA
ISCHEMIA
JAUNDICE
MALARIA
MEASLES
NAUSEA
PARASITE
PLAGUE
PNEUMONIA
RESISTANT
STROKE
VACCINE
WHOOPING COUGH

ABSCESS   BACTERIA   CHRONIC
ANTIBODY   BRUISE   COLD
ATROPHY   CHOLERA   CYST

DOUBLETALK

Homophones are words that share the same pronunciation, no matter how they are spelled. If they are spelled differently then they are called heterographs. Find heterographs meaning:

TO SQUANDER and A PART OF THE BODY

★★★★★ Do the Math by Don Law

ACROSS

1 Belarussian, e.g.
5 Rosette member
10 Castle defense
14 Hayseed
15 Heavenly places
16 Opera singer Haugland
17 $2^2 + 2^3 + 3^3 + 4^3 =$
20 Door-to-door person
21 Jimmy of *The Daily Planet*
22 "Give ___ break!"
23 Have an outstanding figure?
24 In-house
29 Neiman's business partner
33 Light on a strip
34 Pâté base, often
36 Baton Rouge college
37 $12^3 + 16^2 + 20 =$
41 Soak flax
42 Mark Twain, for one
43 Egg-shaped
44 Master thief Lupin
46 To the extreme
49 Tennis player Riglewski
50 Technique
51 Marble-cake pattern
54 Optimistic
59 $3{,}000.006 \times 1{,}000 =$
62 Paperback
63 Diarist Nin
64 City of central Sicily
65 Delany or Carvey
66 3-D feature
67 From ___ to stern

DOWN

1 Sold-out signs
2 J.K. Rowling's Lovegood
3 First lady's son
4 Very strong
5 Calligrapher
6 Icelandic epic
7 Mackerel gull
8 Chemical ending for pent
9 Mind-expanding drug
10 *The Song of the Earth* composer
11 Regatta equipment
12 Arthur of *Hoop Dreams*
13 Jughead is one
18 Computernik
19 In the direction of
23 Prophetic sign
24 Prefix for mural
25 More modern
26 Hits the horn
27 To him: Fr.
28 Kudrow and Simpson
30 Ham spice
31 Typical
32 Curmudgeonly
35 Pottery piece
38 Doorknob
39 Roll topper
40 Destinies
45 "I found it!"
47 Dematerialize
48 Therefore
51 Opposite of port: Abbr.
52 "Stop!"
53 Fairway club
54 Duel invitation
55 Did a dismount
56 "___ it a pity?
57 $1^3 + 2^3 =$
58 More than a quiz
60 Loony
61 Suffix for hero

★ Sudoku Twin

Fill in the grid so that each row, each column and each 3 x 3 frame contains every number from 1 to 9. A sudoku twin is two connected 9 x 9 sudokus.

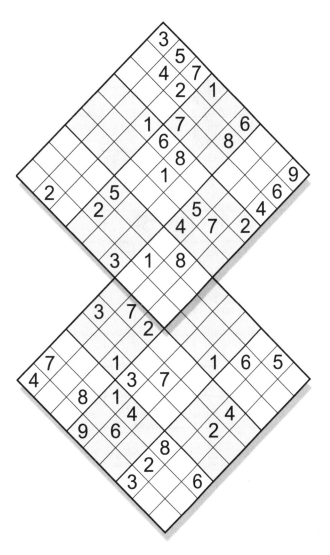

LETTER LINE

Put a letter in each of the squares below to make a word which means "a NATURAL ENVIRONMENT." These numbered clues refer to other words which can be made from the whole.

1 2 7 4 3 5 9 10 FLAT CALM; 9 1 2 7 4 3 5 9 CHEATS; 6 5 7 5 1 9 REPLACES; 6 2 7 9 5 WASH

1	2	3	4	5	6	7	8	9	10

★★ Keep Going

Start on a blank square of your choice and connect as many blank squares as possible with one single continuous line. You can only connect squares along vertical and horizontal lines, not along diagonal lines. You must continue the connecting line up until the next obstacle, i.e., the rim of the box, a black square or a square that has already been used. You can change direction at any obstacle you meet. Each square can be used only once. The number of blank squares that will be left unused is marked in the upper square. There is more than one solution. We show only one solution.

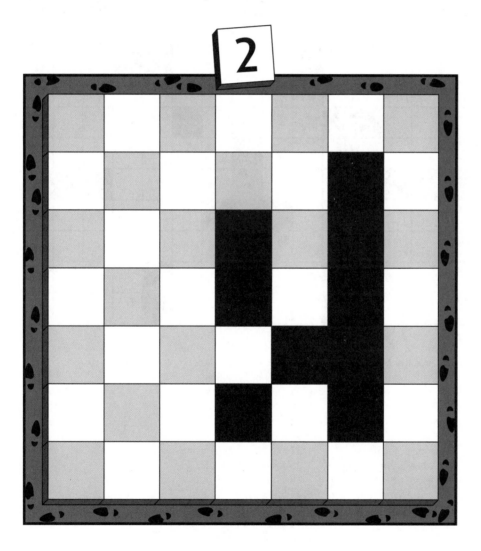

REPOSITION PREPOSITION

Unscramble FARM FOR and find a two-word preposition.

★★★★★ Do More Math by Don Law

ACROSS

1 Throw a fit
5 *Saturday Night Live* bit
10 Cartoon company
14 Soothing additive
15 Fielding-average lowerer
16 Leg bone
17 $260^2 + 13^3 + 203 =$
20 Goober pea
21 Makes one out of two
22 The same: Lat.
24 New newts
25 Sweet amber wine
28 Put on display
32 Not to be missed
33 Art ___
35 Rosary bead
36 $2^2 + 16^3 =$
40 Aegean Sea island
41 Pierre's papa
42 Nymph in myth
43 Red star in Scorpius
46 With keen interest
48 Restaurant waiting areas
49 Czech, e.g.
50 Take off the gloves?
53 Goes out of focus
57 $3,100 \times 20,000 =$
61 Nobelist Metchnikoff
62 Condor's clutcher
63 Poetic Norse tales
64 He's the Lone Ranger
65 Supplement
66 Very profound

DOWN

1 Carpentry file
2 Shelterward
3 PBS science program
4 Most microscopic
5 Hunting dog
6 Horn in
7 Leftover for Fido
8 "I like, I like"
9 Fancy-schmancy
10 Lend a hand
11 Yellow-breasted bird
12 "You Will Be ___": Faith Hill
13 Odds partner
18 "The full monty" state
19 "Once more ___ the breach ...": Shak.
23 Insanity
24 Engravers
25 Godfather's group
26 ___ for the Misbegotten: O'Neill
27 Fred of Limp Bizkit
29 Did some rowing
30 Of an eye layer
31 A Roosevelt
34 Auction ender
37 *H.M.S. Pinafore* is one
38 Cricket ump's call
39 Slobbered
44 Died down
45 Risqué
47 White elephant, e.g.
50 Software buyer
51 Khartoum river
52 Form of 62
54 ___-de-camp
55 Badgered
56 Gingery cookie
58 Bankroll
59 Like Father William
60 Pithy remark

★ Monkey Business

Some of the older students have been monkeying about with the BEST KIDS BOOKS titles list in the library. Can you fix it?

1 RARE SHOW
  by MICHAEL MORPURGO

2 SPICIER ZOO GAZE AND THE GURU
  by MARGARET REY

3 DRIP IF OK MAIDWAY
  by JEFF KINNEY

4 PIG FACE AND FROM THUG
  by PETER YARROW

5 IF NICE DEAR
  by ERIN HUNTER

BLOCK ANAGRAM

Form the word that is described in the brackets with the letters above the grid. Extra letters are already in the right place.

NOT NAOMI (naming)

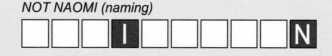

★ Clothing

All the words are hidden vertically, horizontally or diagonally—in both directions. The letters that remain unused form a sentence from left to right.

```
F U N D E R W E A R O T R S O
M L I N G E R I E E E M A E N
S W E A T E R P T H O H E H T
S I S E H I P N C N S A N R S
E E L T S I O O O S W E E O N
T I A A Z I R M L E P B C I B
E E D S H C I D A C B K E L O
L R N S O K F V R U S C O L O
E U A S T N E H R E I U N G B
I F S T T H S A T T S H T E U
S Y N O T T O C W E T S U I T
U T P C E M B R O I D E R N T
R L R K I L T O E U T A B W O
E L I I U N I F O R M O A O N
W M T N H O F T I T B M N D S
E E E G E S K C A L S M A N D
A N C S A N R K N I T E O I N
R D T S R E M R A W G E L S O
```

FUR
HAT
KILT
KIMONO
KNIT
LEATHER
LEG WARMERS
LEISUREWEAR
LINEN
LINGERIE
MEND
RUBBER
SANDALS
SEASONS
SHIRT
SLACKS
SOCKS
SOMBRERO
STOCKINGS
SWEATER
TURBAN
UNDERWEAR
UNIFORM
WEAVE
WET SUIT
ZIPPER

BLOUSE
BOOTS
BUTTONS

COTTON
CROCHET
DOWN

DRESS
EMBROIDER
FASHION

UNCANNY TURN

Rearrange the letters of the word below to form a cognate anagram, one which is related or connected in meaning to the original phrase. The answer can be one or more words.

BUT SLY

★★★★★ Full Name Please by John McCarthy

ACROSS

1 Retired NBA cager O'Neal
5 Soccer positions
10 Olympic queen
14 Diamond Head locale
15 Defeatist phrase
16 Throughout
17 Wings
18 Small crowd
19 Mother of Artemis
20 Gray general
23 Mary Lincoln, ___ Todd
24 Mrs. Hoover
25 Shaw's *Major ___*
29 Cork in a bottle
33 In a whirl
34 Doldrums
36 Sony rival
37 Housecoat
38 Far from reticent
39 In no time
40 1300 hours
41 "Lady Marmalade" singer LaBelle
42 Lurk in the shadows
43 *The Graduate* director
45 Happens to, as if by fate
47 NYSE newcomer
48 Hide ___ hair
49 *Fargo* star
58 First brother
59 Téa of *Jurassic Park III*
60 Figure skater Kulik
61 Parking penalty
62 Batch from the Queen of Hearts
63 Hexagram
64 Pre-1917 monarch
65 Start of an attack
66 Parka part

DOWN

1 Fly like an eagle
2 2009 Beyoncé hit
3 Starbuck's skipper
4 Head of the hive
5 Sour
6 Throb
7 ATM insert
8 Felt in one's bones
9 Catfooted
10 Delay
11 Daredevil Knievel
12 Nerve bundle
13 Islands SW of New Guinea
21 Not virtual
22 Down Under springers
25 British nobleman
26 Quaker's Rice-___
27 Medieval violin
28 Touches on
29 Colonial title in India
30 Puffed up
31 French school
32 Break ___ (defect)
35 D-Day craft
38 Home of Stanford University
39 Brush
41 Alan Arkin film
42 Short-runway craft
44 *The Hospital* director
46 Join
49 Float, as an aroma
50 Storklike wader
51 Olin in *The Reader*
52 Spiteful
53 ___ d'oeuvres
54 Poker stake
55 Vocal range
56 Arrivederci
57 Not quite a meter

★★ Sunny Weather

Where will the sun shine? With the knowledge that each arrow points to a place where a symbol should be, can you locate the sunny spots? The symbols cannot be next to each other vertically, horizontally or diagonally. A symbol cannot be placed on top of an arrow. We show one symbol.

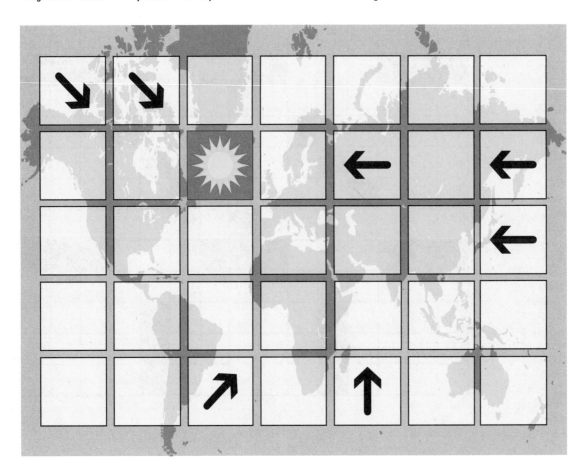

ONE LETTER LESS OR MORE

The word on the right side contains the letters of the word on the left side plus or minus the letter in the middle. One letter is already in the right place.

M A D H O U S E +I ☐ ☐ U ☐ ☐ ☐ ☐

★★★ Concentration—Squared

Divide each square into four identical parts (see the two examples). Try this in nine different ways without mirroring or rotating the page.

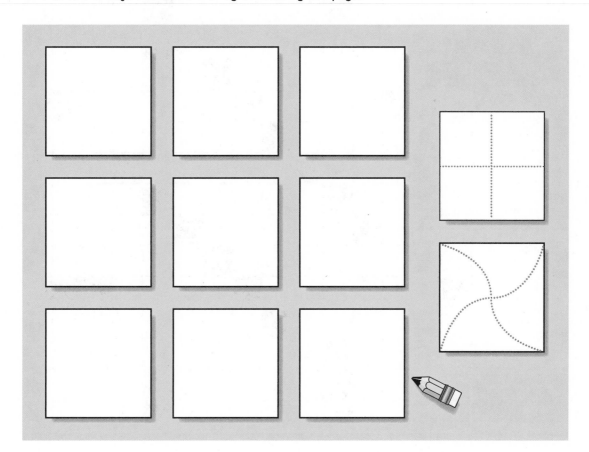

CHANGE ONE

Change one letter in each of these two words to form a common two-word phrase. There may be more than one possible answer.

MUST LANCE

★★★★★ Quote Unquote by John M. Samson

ACROSS

1 Placid
5 Did a farrier's job
10 Branchlet
14 Indonesian islands
15 Maui veranda
16 Table d'___
17 "Politics is applesauce." source
19 Bower flower
20 Saves from ruin
21 ___ Knight & the Pips
23 *If ___ the Zoo*: Seuss
24 With indifference
25 Like booty
28 Coastal cliff
31 Bookstore passageway
32 Edie of *The Sopranos*
33 Hawaii's Mauna ___
34 Triathlon event
35 Borden cow
36 Novel essence
37 Big Band ___
38 Nocturnal scavenger
39 Witherspoon in *Pleasantville*
40 First to arrive
42 Large headline
43 Value
44 Blanched
45 Take off
47 Crop-dusting need
51 Join metal to metal
52 "War settles nothing." source
54 Store cargo
55 Surviving mark
56 Planters' purchases
57 Husky's burden
58 Gabby of westerns
59 Part of an ultimatum

DOWN

1 Crow cries
2 Five-star Las Vegas hotel
3 Be indolent
4 *Moby-Dick* author
5 Ad campaign "hook"
6 Links legend Walter
7 Change for a five
8 Play it by ___
9 Ignominy
10 One in bondage
11 "I am two with nature." source
12 Eenie
13 Thousands, in slang
18 Sidewalk show
22 Venice Film Festival site
24 One of the Ephrons
25 Delhi dress
26 Royal crown
27 "The world is a stage, but the play is badly cast." source
28 "It ___ hit me yet"
29 End of one's rope?
30 Postal machine
32 Meat
35 Upper canines
36 Cruz in *Nine*
38 "Java" trumpeter Al
39 Fiennes or Wiggum
41 Weighted down
42 Noble partner
44 Fragment
45 Punches in the shop
46 Saltimbocca meat
47 Have ___ in (influence)
48 Military no-no
49 New Jersey NBA team
50 Limerick language
53 *Deathtrap* playwright Levin

★★ The Puzzled Librarian

The new library assistant accidentally bumped into the Good Reads notice board, and the magnetic letters all fell off. The librarian remembered the authors' names, but needs some help to get the titles right, as the chief librarian will be back in ten minutes!

GOOD READS NOTICE BOARD

1 GOOD RATTLING WHITE HOT THREAT by Stieg Larsson
2 INCENSES OF HOT by John Grisham
3 BEAUTY NOBLER HATER by Eric Van Lustbader
4 ITCHINGLY THINKING DAFT BRUTE by Kate Jacobs
5 YO HO HO ELEVEN TRUE WIT by Emily Giffin
6 MOLEST BY SLOTH by Dan Brown
7 THE RUDE DEMON by Stephen King
8 HELL AGED SANE DEATH by Jack Higgins
9 REGIMENT HANG by JP Donleavy
10 THROB THIS NERD by Colleen McCullough

CHANGELINGS

Each of the three lines of letters below spell words which have a clothing connection, but the letters have been mixed up. Four letters from the first word are now in the third line, four letters from the third word are in the second line and four letters from the second word are in the first line. The remaining letters are in their original places. What are the words?

B U H T A N C O K E
P N L T E R N E T P
T I O S H R I L E S

★ Elton John

All the words are hidden vertically, horizontally or diagonally—in both directions. The letters that remain unused form a sentence from left to right.

```
B T H N Y E N A M E E L L T O
A O N J I M S I N G E R O H N
I N R S A P M C O I M B I N A
T O A D I A U A N I O P N O S
F D E I E S C A R I B O U L E
T A O R D R D I T G N D D E S
A R U L N E S W R A N I D L S
N O V E L V O O I T N U G D A
T D T N J O E Y N G N M N H L
O L O N H C V G E G H E N E G
B E M O B A E O L C I T C R S
E D M N E F I L M R A R H C T
R Y Y S C A L O F T W S A U E
N U U I O N E S C O L L R L U
I M S L E S B E A G B U I E D
E U E S S F R U O U M H T S V
M T H G I N K L M I S F Y I R
D R O F T A W B S T G R O U P
```

DANIEL
DIANA
DUETS
DWIGHT
ECCENTRIC
ELDORADO
FANS
FILM
FRIENDS
GLASSES
GRAMMY
HERCULES
KNIGHT
LENNON
LEVON
MUSE
MUSIC
PODIUM
RUSSIA
SINGER
TAUPIN
TOMMY
TOUR
VERSACE
WATFORD

AIDA
ALBUM
BELIEVE

BERNIE
BLUESOLOGY
BORDERSONG

CARIBOU
CHARITY
COVERS

DELETE ONE

Delete one letter from LETS RUSH and find a tricky operator.

★★★★ Futoshiki

Fill in the 5 x 5 grid with the numbers from 1 to 5 once per row and column, while following the greater than/lesser than symbols shown. There is only one valid solution that can be reached through logic and clear thinking alone!

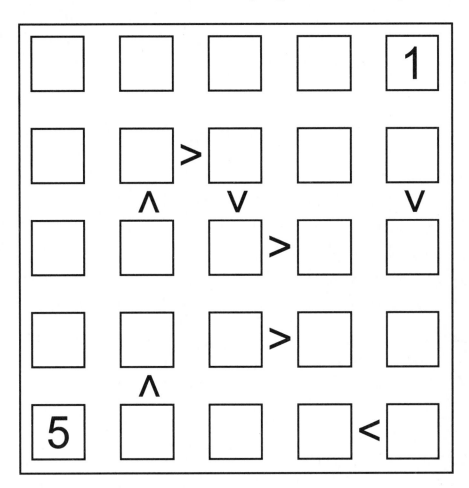

DOODLE PUZZLE

A doodle puzzle is a combination of images, letters and/or numbers that represent a word or a concept. If you cannot solve a doodle puzzle, do not look at the answer right away. Think hard—and outside the box.

★ Word Pyramid

Each word in the pyramid has the letters of the word above it, plus a new letter.

G

(1) as an example
(2) acquire
(3) movable barrier in a fence
(4) broker
(5) feeding
(6) time of origin
(7) travel on water

LETTERBLOCKS

Move the letterblocks around so that words are formed on top and below that you can associate with language.

S N A E L I H
S P G S N I H

★★★ BrainSnack®—Directions

You are in a city where all the streets are equally long and where all the streets cross at right angles. On each corner of the street there is a signpost. You start your journey at signpost 1. After which signpost (2–12) will you find yourself back in starting position?

CHANGE ONE

Change one letter in each of these two words to form a common two-word phrase. There may be more than one possible answer.

TEAR SIT

★★★★★ Celebrity Perfumes by Mary Leonard

ACROSS

1 Tim of *Private Practice*
5 Global area
9 Dull finish
14 Ersatz spread
15 Madras wrap
16 *Pal Joey* novelist
17 "Shine" is her perfume
19 Burgomaster
20 Spa on Lake Geneva
21 Camelot wizard
22 2012 Olympics host country
25 Place on the beach
26 Second crop
27 Barely sufficient
29 Cut of meat
32 La Scala stagings
34 Some are liberal
35 ___-fi film
36 Author Fleming
37 Venus neighbor
39 Humorist
40 ___ *for Corpse*: Grafton
41 Nullify
42 Like disciplinarians
45 Picnic pest
46 Clown pole
48 Long arm
49 Turn outward
51 Smash
53 Best way to drive
55 Jumped
56 Reflection
57 "Meow!" is her perfume
61 Grannies
62 "What ___ could I do?"
63 Poseidon's mom
64 Smiles
65 "Here ___ nothing!"
66 Linger in the tub

DOWN

1 "What was I thinking?"
2 Ginger ___
3 Hilo souvenir
4 Mountain warbler
5 Show politeness at the door
6 Caesar and Waldorf, e.g.
7 "___ Away": Britney Spears
8 Use crosshairs
9 Instants
10 Arthur Ashe's ___ *Road to Glory*
11 "Wonderstruck" is her perfume
12 *Star Trek: TNG* empath
13 Merit pay
18 Eric Trump's mother
21 Calendar pages
22 Beethoven's Third
23 Feeling ___ (drunk)
24 "Harajuku Lovers" is her perfume
25 Shopping aid
28 Yule tune
30 Frozen hanger
31 Hostile
33 Watchman
38 Colliery passage
41 Good for nothing
43 *The Sound of Music* family
44 Actors John and Jason
47 Fly of Africa
50 Human herbivore
52 Helen in *Airport*
53 Croon
54 Bose of Bose Corp.
55 *Le Roi d'Ys* composer
57 Beer holder
58 Greek P
59 Stephen in *The Heavy*
60 Tibetan ox

PAGE 15

2011 Comedy Films

S	K	I	D		A	T	T	A	R		E	T	N	A
I	A	G	O		P	O	R	N	O		R	O	O	D
T	H	E	M	U	P	P	E	T	S		A	W	E	D
A	N	T	I	L	L	E	S		E	A	S	E	L	S
			N	E	E	R		L	A	M	E	R		
W	A	Y	A	N	S		B	A	N	I	S	H	E	S
I	D	O	N	T		C	A	R	N	E		E	E	C
L	O	U	T		M	A	N	G	E		M	I	L	A
E	R	N		B	I	N	G	O		P	O	S	E	R
S	E	G	M	E	N	T	S		S	E	N	T	R	Y
			A	U	D	I	O		C	O	T	S		
L	A	D	L	E	S		R	E	L	A	T	I	O	N
A	L	U	I		T	H	E	D	I	L	E	M	M	A
M	I	L	S		E	B	B	E	D		R	A	I	N
B	E	T	H		R	O	A	D	S		S	S	T	S

PAGE 16

Number Cluster

8	6	4	3	5	7
8	6	4	3	5	7
8	6	4	3	5	7
8	6	4	5	5	7
8	6	6	2	7	7
8	8	8	2	1	7

CONNECT TWO
FINE MESS, COLD SWEAT, RANDOM ORDER, VIRTUAL REALITY

PAGE 17

BrainSnack®—Every Second Counts

21. The sum of the numbers making up the hours, minutes and seconds equals the number on the rider's back, and all hours, minutes and seconds start with 0, 1 and 2 respectively.

DOUBLETALK
REED/READ

PAGE 18

Geometry 101

C	L	A	P	S		C	O	P	Y		J	E	R	K
R	E	M	A	P		A	L	E	E		O	G	E	E
O	V	I	N	E		N	A	L	A		B	O	N	Y
C	I	R	C	L	E	O	F	F	R	I	E	N	D	S
			A	L	O	E		L	A	T				
B	R	O	K	E	N		N	E	I	G	H	B	O	R
O	O	H	E	D		P	O	R	N	O		R	P	I
L	A	Y	S		C	L	U	N	G		R	A	I	D
U	S	O		B	O	O	N	E		B	E	N	N	E
S	T	U	D	E	N	T	S		D	A	N	D	E	R
			E	L	F		K	E	N	O				
T	R	A	F	A	L	G	A	R	S	Q	U	A	R	E
R	O	L	E		I	O	L	E		U	N	C	A	P
I	V	A	N		C	R	O	W		E	C	O	L	E
P	E	N	D		T	E	T	E		T	E	P	E	E

PAGE 19

Summer

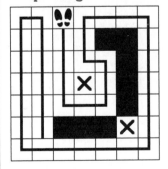

In the southern hemisphere it is high summer during our winter months of December, January and February.

MISSING LETTER MOTTO
BE PREPARED (Boy Scouts)

PAGE 20

Keep Going

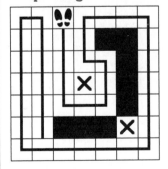

UNCANNY TURN
INCOME TAXES

PAGE 21

European Fare

S	L	A	P		S	T	E	E	P		M	E	D	O
T	A	L	E		L	O	N	E	R		I	V	O	R
I	T	A	L	I	A	N	D	R	E	S	S	I	N	G
R	E	S	E	R	V	E	S		M	O	T	L	E	Y
			O	E	R		H	I	R	E				
B	A	S	I	N	S		A	B	E	R	R	A	N	T
A	L	T	A		S	T	O	R	E		L	I	E	
S	P	A	N	I	S	H	O	M	E	L	E	T	T	E
I	H	R		C	L	I	M	B		K	E	E	N	
C	A	R	T	O	O	N	S		S	H	E	R	R	Y
			O	N	U	S		J	A	Y				
E	C	H	O	I	C		S	U	B	M	E	R	G	E
F	R	E	N	C	H	O	N	I	O	N	S	O	U	P
T	O	R	I		E	V	I	C	T		M	I	N	E
S	P	E	E		D	A	T	E	S		E	L	S	E

PAGE 22

Sudoku

2	5	7	3	8	4	6	1	9
4	1	6	9	7	5	3	8	2
3	9	8	1	6	2	7	4	5
9	8	5	7	3	1	4	2	6
7	2	3	4	9	6	8	5	1
1	6	4	5	2	8	9	7	3
8	4	1	6	5	9	2	3	7
6	3	2	8	1	7	5	9	4
5	7	9	2	4	3	1	6	8

BLOCK ANAGRAM
ELECTION

PAGE 23

Sport Maze

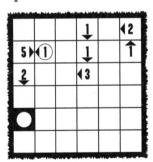

SANDWICH
AGE

PAGE 24
Down Under Stars

```
B O I L   E G G A R   T S A R
A C T A   V I R G O   S U R E
T H E B E E G E E S   E T T A
T O M O R R O W   E I T H E R
      R I T T   M A N S E
A T H E N S   W A N D E R E D
P E E R S   C O R N Y   L E A
H A L S   L O R R E   C A L L
I S E   D A N D Y   R E N E E
D E N T I S T S   S U N D R Y
      R E E V E   P O S T
A V E R S E   N A U S E A T E
C E D E   G R E G N O R M A N
R I D S   A I M E D   E M I T
E N Y A   S P O T S   D O L E
```

PAGE 25
Word Sudoku

```
D F Q T S E I P K
P I K Q D F S T E
E T S I P K D Q F
Q S T K F I E D P
I K D P E S Q F T
F P E D Q T K S I
S E P F I D T K Q
T Q I S K P F E D
K D F E T Q P I S
```

ONE LETTER LESS OR MORE
SANDBAG

PAGE 26
BrainSnack®—Fast Lane

09.78 seconds. Use the remaining numbers on the bathing caps from right to left.

CONNECT TWO
DETAILED SUMMARY, SPEED LIMIT, FAST FOOD, SLUMBER PARTY

PAGE 27
Afterlife

```
S C A T S   T O M B   I K O N
A A R A U   O M O O   N I N O
K A F K A   W I T T   N E M O
I N S E V E N T H H E A V E N
      C E L S   B E R T
S O M A L I   M A R I E T T E
O T A R Y   M A L E S   R I M
S A G E   G O U L D   H O M O
A R I   D O O R S   D I V O T
D U C H O V N Y   A R S E N E
      A D E S   A S A P
H E L L O R H I G H W A T E R
E V I L   N I C E   E N O L A
R E D O   O N A N   R I G O R
B R O W   R E N T   S C O N E
```

PAGE 28
Binairo

```
0 1 1 0 1 1 0 1 0 1 0 0
1 0 1 0 1 0 1 1 0 0 1 0
0 1 0 1 0 0 1 0 1 1 0 1
1 0 0 1 0 1 0 1 0 0 1 1
0 1 1 0 1 0 1 0 1 0 1 0
1 0 0 1 0 1 0 0 1 1 0 1
0 0 1 0 1 0 1 1 0 1 1 0
0 1 1 0 0 1 0 0 1 0 1 1
1 0 0 1 0 1 1 0 1 1 0 0
0 1 1 0 1 0 1 1 0 0 1 0
1 1 0 1 0 1 0 0 1 0 0 1
1 0 0 1 1 0 0 1 0 1 0 1
```

REPOSITION PREPOSITION
IN LIEU OF

PAGE 29
Spot the Differences

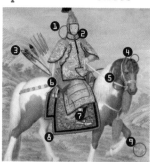

DELETE ONE
Delete S and find SURGICAL INSTRUMENT

PAGE 30
Irate

```
F R E T   D R O L L   T W I G
R A R E   E E R I E   O R S O
A N G R Y B I R D S   M A L E
      M E A N   S E D A T E S
A D M I T S       E T H
M E A T I E R   S C R O O G E
A N D E S   Y O K U M   F A X
J I M S   A D V I L   S K Y E
O S A   A G E O F   O T H E R
R E G U L A R   F A R E A S T
      A N A   T A I N T S
H A Z I N G S   V O N N
I R I S   R A G I N G B U L L
D I N O   U V U L A   O R E O
E D E N   B E T E L   K N O W
```

PAGE 31
Cage the Animals

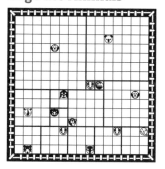

DOUBLETALK
HOUR/OUR

PAGE 32
Tolkein

It took Tolkien almost ten years to write his voluminous and mysterious masterpiece *Lord of the Rings*.

CHANGE ONE
COME BACK

PAGE 33

Sunny Weather

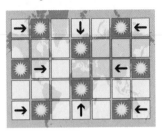

SANDWICH

MIND

PAGE 34

Oh Oh!

A	L	A	R		B	A	B	E	S		A	H	O	Y
P	A	C	E		E	R	E	C	T		F	U	S	S
S	W	I	T	C	H	E	R	O	O		F	L	E	E
E	N	D	U	R	I	N	G		M	A	I	L	E	R
		R	U	N	T		S	A	B	R	A			
D	A	W	N	E	D		C	U	C	U	M	B	E	R
E	T	H	E	L		O	U	G	H	T		A	X	E
M	O	O	D		S	A	R	A	S		O	L	I	N
U	N	O		M	A	T	E	R		C	L	O	S	E
R	E	P	A	I	R	E	D		C	O	Y	O	T	E
			D	U	R	A	N		B	A	L	M		
O	B	E	R	O	N		E	U	R	O	P	E	A	N
D	O	D	O		D	I	D	G	E	R	I	D	O	O
D	O	O	R		O	D	I	L	E		C	A	N	S
S	T	O	A		N	I	T	E	R		S	M	E	E

PAGE 35

Kakuro

4	1	2		8	6	5
	2	9		2	9	
7	3	4	6		7	6
1			9	7	8	
		8	5	9		
8	6	9		8	2	4
3	1			1	3	

LETTERBLOCKS

MANAGER
TEACHER

PAGE 36

BrainSnack®—Slots

Wheel 5. To be identical the lowest BAR on the strip of this wheel must be replaced with a dollar sign.

LETTER LINE

FREELOADER; ORDEAL; READER; FEDERAL; DEALER

PAGE 37

Cities of the World

I	R	A	Q		C	R	A	M	P		S	C	A	T
S	U	L	U		H	O	R	A	L		A	A	B	A
A	D	D	I	S	A	B	A	B	A		U	S	E	R
R	E	A	C	T	I	O	N		C	I	C	A	D	A
		K	E	N	T		C	A	L	E	B			
M	O	D	E	L	S		W	A	T	E	R	L	O	O
A	B	U	S	E		F	A	M	E	D		A	D	D
N	E	S	T		C	A	R	E	D		S	N	E	E
O	S	S		M	O	R	E	L		P	E	C	O	S
F	E	E	L	I	N	G	S		B	A	N	A	N	A
	L	E	N	T	O		M	A	N	S				
S	E	D	A	T	E		H	E	R	E	U	N	T	O
I	V	O	R		S	A	I	N	T	L	O	U	I	S
T	E	R	N		T	E	N	S	E		U	K	E	S
A	R	F	S		S	I	T	A	R		S	E	R	A

PAGE 38

Keep Going

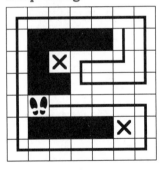

UNCANNY TURN

A PSYCHIATRIST

PAGE 39

Sudoku

2	6	8	1	9	4	3	7	5
3	7	1	5	8	2	6	4	9
5	4	9	6	7	3	2	1	8
9	3	4	7	2	1	8	5	6
1	8	6	3	4	5	9	2	7
7	5	2	9	6	8	1	3	4
6	2	3	4	5	9	7	8	1
4	1	7	8	3	6	5	9	2
8	9	5	2	1	7	4	6	3

CONNECT TWO

ACTIVE RETIREMENT, ACCURATE ESTIMATE, FREE MARKET, GOOD GRIEF

PAGE 40

Seasonal

I	M	A	C		T	O	R	A	H		A	D	A	M
N	O	A	H		O	R	O	N	O		S	O	R	A
S	P	R	I	N	G	B	O	K	S		S	N	I	P
			M	O	O	S		A	S	C	E	N	D	S
B	R	E	N	T					E	T	A			
R	E	D	E	E	M		S	T	R	E	S	S	E	D
E	D	G	Y		A	D	O	R	E	S		U	T	E
A	S	A	S		C	E	L	E	B		I	M	A	N
T	E	R		C	R	E	A	T	E		M	M	I	I
H	A	W	T	H	O	R	N		L	A	P	E	L	S
		I	R	E					P	E	R	S	E	
B	E	N	E	F	I	T		U	R	A	L			
A	N	T	A		T	H	E	F	A	L	L	G	U	Y
N	Y	E	T		E	A	T	O	N		E	R	S	E
G	A	R	Y		M	I	D	S	T		D	U	E	T

PAGE 41

Futoshiki

4	5	3	1	2
2 < 3	1	5	4
5 > 4	2	3	1
3	1	4	2	5
1	2	5 > 4 > 3

ONE LETTER LESS OR MORE

MEDICAL

PAGE 42

Word Sudoku

G	I	A	X	E	L	O	T	S
T	E	L	O	A	S	X	G	I
S	X	O	G	I	T	L	E	A
A	O	S	L	X	E	T	I	G
I	L	G	T	O	A	S	X	E
X	T	E	I	S	G	A	L	O
E	G	T	S	L	O	I	A	X
O	A	I	E	T	X	G	S	L
L	S	X	A	G	I	E	O	T

BLOCK ANAGRAM
DEMOCRATIC

PAGE 43

BrainSnack®—Foul Play

3. A foul is committed in every zone of 3 by 3 squares.

SANDWICH
MARK

PAGE 44

Holiday Songs

A	M	A	H		A	L	A	N	A		W	E	E	P
L	O	R	I		B	O	S	O	M		E	A	R	L
B	I	N	G	C	R	O	S	B	Y		A	R	L	O
A	L	E	H	O	U	S	E		S	A	L	T	E	D
		T	A	P	E		S	M	I	T	H			
O	B	J	E	C	T		A	L	A	N	H	A	L	E
F	R	O	S	H		S	H	I	R	T		K	E	L
F	I	S	T		U	N	A	P	T		M	I	N	T
E	D	H		O	N	E	R	S		S	E	T	T	O
R	E	G	A	R	D	E	D		P	A	R	T	O	N
		R	U	L	E	R		B	L	O	C			
P	O	O	R	E	R		B	R	U	N	E	T	T	E
L	O	B	O		C	E	L	I	N	E	D	I	O	N
U	L	A	R		U	S	I	N	G		E	L	M	O
S	A	N	A		T	E	P	E	E		S	L	E	W

PAGE 45

Cage the Animals

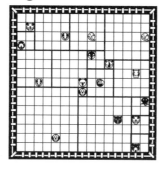

FRIENDS?
Each can have the suffix -ATE to form a new word.

PAGE 46

Binairo

O	I	I	O	O	I	I	O	I	O	I
I	I	O	O	I	O	O	I	I	O	I
I	O	I	I	O	I	O	I	O	I	O
O	I	O	I	I	O	I	O	O	I	I
O	O	I	O	I	I	O	I	I	O	I
I	I	O	I	O	I	I	O	I	O	O
O	O	I	I	O	O	I	I	O	I	I
I	O	I	O	I	I	O	I	O	I	O
O	I	O	I	I	O	I	O	I	O	I
I	O	I	O	O	I	I	O	I	I	O
I	I	O	I	I	O	O	I	O	I	O

DOUBLETALK
CREEK/CREAK

PAGE 47

Antagonists

P	A	G	E		C	R	E	E	P		A	G	E	D
I	B	E	X		Y	A	L	T	A		R	O	T	E
C	A	L	H	O	C	K	L	E	Y		D	R	U	B
			O	G	L	E	S		C	R	E	D	I	T
C	H	A	R	R	E	D		C	H	I	N	O		
R	A	N	T	E	D		C	H	E	F		N	U	B
I	N	N	E	S		E	R	E	C	T		G	P	O
S	K	I	D		W	R	E	A	K		N	E	R	O
P	I	E		J	A	N	E	T		Y	O	K	O	S
Y	E	W		E	N	I	D		P	E	C	K	A	T
		I	N	A	N	E		S	E	N	H	O	R	S
G	A	L	E	N	A		A	O	R	T	A			
I	N	K	S		B	I	F	F	T	A	N	N	E	N
S	T	E	T		E	M	A	I	L		C	A	V	E
T	E	S	S		S	P	R	A	Y		E	P	E	E

PAGE 48

BrainSnack®—Spot the Lily

Water lily 5. A petal is missing next to the number five.

MISSING LETTER MOTTO
TO PROTECT AND TO SERVE (police departments)

PAGE 49

Rivers

The left bank and right bank of a river are determined from the viewpoint of the source.

DELETE ONE
Delete I and find LUDICROUS

PAGE 50

Britannia

M	A	R	C		S	T	R	A	W		H	A	N	S
O	D	O	R		E	R	I	C	H		A	R	O	W
S	A	T	O		N	I	T	T	I		P	A	R	A
T	H	E	S	C	O	T	T	I	S	H	P	L	A	Y
			S	O	R	E		T	E	E				
M	A	R	I	S	A		A	T	L	A	N	T	I	C
A	M	E	N	T		F	L	E	E	T		I	D	A
M	A	R	G		E	E	L	E	R		T	R	E	T
B	T	U		M	Y	R	O	N		C	H	E	A	T
O	I	N	T	M	E	N	T		D	R	E	S	S	Y
			O	C	T		H	E	A	R				
P	R	I	N	C	E	S	S	O	F	W	A	L	E	S
R	I	G	G		E	L	I	T	E		V	I	T	A
A	L	O	U		T	O	N	E	R		E	L	A	N
M	E	R	E		H	E	E	L	S		N	O	S	E

PAGE 51

BrainSnack®—Name It

V. All the letters in the alphabet are used, only the letter V is missing.

CONNECT TWO

ALMOST EXACTLY, LADIES MAN, LIQUID GAS, MUD BATH

PAGE 52

Sudoku

6	9	4	2	8	7	3	1	5
5	2	1	3	6	9	4	7	8
7	8	3	4	1	5	9	2	6
9	3	2	1	5	6	8	4	7
1	7	5	8	4	3	6	9	2
8	4	6	9	7	2	1	5	3
2	6	9	7	3	4	5	8	1
4	5	8	6	2	1	7	3	9
3	1	7	5	9	8	2	6	4

UNCANNY TURN

MANY A TRUE WORD IS SPOKEN IN JEST

PAGE 53

Give and Take

R	A	M	S		A	U	N	T	S		L	A	N	G
I	L	I	A		S	T	E	E	P		I	G	O	R
G	I	R	L		T	E	A	S	E		G	I	G	I
G	I	V	E	S	U	P	T	H	E	G	H	O	S	T
			S	I	T			C	O	T				
S	C	A	M	P	E	R		C	H	A	S	T	E	N
I	R	M	A	S		E	G	R	E	T		O	X	O
G	O	O	N		F	L	E	A	S		U	R	U	S
H	O	R		S	A	I	L	S		S	P	A	D	E
S	K	E	P	T	I	C		S	L	A	S	H	E	S
		E	A	T			E	S	T					
T	A	K	E	T	H	E	H	I	G	H	R	O	A	D
E	M	I	L		F	L	O	R	A		E	E	L	Y
S	M	E	E		U	B	O	A	T		A	N	T	A
T	O	L	D		L	A	P	S	E		M	O	O	N

PAGE 54

Word Sudoku

V	G	N	F	Y	R	D	E	I
Y	E	I	G	N	D	V	F	R
D	F	R	V	I	E	Y	G	N
F	R	V	I	D	N	G	Y	E
E	Y	G	R	F	V	N	I	D
I	N	D	E	G	Y	F	R	V
G	V	E	N	R	F	I	D	Y
R	I	Y	D	V	G	E	N	F
N	D	F	Y	E	I	R	V	G

SANDWICH

LINE

PAGE 55

Sport Maze

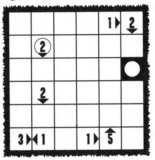

REPOSITION PREPOSITION

ON TOP OF

PAGE 56

Golden Globe Nominees

G	R	A	M		A	M	I	G	O		S	A	C	K
L	U	G	E		T	O	N	A	L		A	L	A	I
U	S	E	R		T	A	F	F	Y		T	E	S	S
T	H	E	I	D	E	S	O	F	M	A	R	C	H	
			D	E	N			P	T	A				
M	A	T	I	L	D	A		A	I	R	P	O	R	T
E	L	I	A		S	I	N	A	I		R	U	E	
M	I	D	N	I	G	H	T	I	N	P	A	R	I	S
O	N	E		L	O	E	S	S		M	I	N	T	
S	E	S	S	I	O	N		E	M	B	A	S	S	Y
			W	A	S			O	A	R				
		T	H	E	D	E	S	C	E	N	D	A	N	T	S
C	O	E	D		E	L	O	P	E		N	A	R	A
P	O	R	E		G	O	O	E	Y		T	R	A	M
A	N	O	N		G	E	N	E	S		H	Y	P	E

PAGE 57

BrainSnack®—How Cheesy!

Flag 5. All the flags have the same colors and are divided into six planes.

LETTERBLOCKS

FIREFLY
TERMITE

PAGE 58

Sudoku Twin

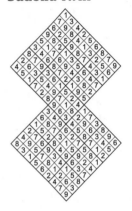

CHANGE ONE

FLIP SIDE

PAGE 59

Pretty Cheesy

M	E	S	H		C	L	A	P	S		A	Q	U	A
A	D	I	A		R	A	D	I	O		S	U	N	G
I	N	N	S		A	B	O	M	B		C	E	D	E
L	A	S	A	G	N	E		A	R	I	O	S	O	S
			S	H	E	L	F		I	O	T	A		
M	O	C	H	A	S		O	W	E	N		D	I	G
A	H	O	O	T		S	N	I	T	S		I	D	O
D	A	R	T		G	O	D	L	Y		G	L	E	E
A	R	D		S	H	O	U	T		S	O	L	A	R
M	A	O		P	A	T	E		S	H	O	A	L	S
		N	A	A	N		S	A	P	I	D			
H	A	B	I	T	A	T		C	A	N	N	O	L	I
A	W	L	S		I	O	W	A	S		E	L	A	N
N	O	E	L		A	N	A	R	M		S	I	N	K
G	L	U	E		N	I	X	E	S		S	O	D	A

PAGE 60

Sunny Weather

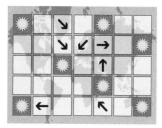

CONNECT TWO

MINOR MIRACLE, NEVER AGAIN, REQUIRED DONATION, AMICABLE DIVORCE

PAGE 61

BrainSnack®—Flag It!

09. The number on the bottom of a flag is the sum of the digits of the numbers on identically colored areas on the top part of a flag.

DOUBLETALK

FORE/FOUR

PAGE 62

Safe Code

3. Ten is added to 13 to get 23 and to 23 to get 33 and 33 to get 43 and 43 to get 53.

BLOCK ANAGRAM

REPUBLICAN

PAGE 63

Themeless

A	M	O	K		S	T	I	N	G		P	S	I	S
T	O	N	I		H	A	G	A	R		A	A	R	E
E	V	E	N		E	C	O	N	O	M	I	C	A	L
N	E	I	G	H	B	O	R		C	A	N	C	E	L
			S	E	A	M		T	E	N	T	H		
S	E	P	T	A		A	F	O	R	E	S	A	I	D
E	R	R	O	R	S		U	N	I	T		R	N	A
N	O	O	N		T	E	R	S	E		M	I	N	I
O	D	S		M	E	D	O		S	C	E	N	E	S
R	E	C	E	I	V	E	R	S		L	E	E	R	Y
		I	N	T	E	R		T	H	A	T			
H	A	U	L	E	D		P	R	O	M	I	S	E	D
A	N	T	I	S	O	C	I	A	L		N	A	R	A
C	O	T	S		R	A	P	I	D		G	R	I	N
K	N	O	T		E	D	E	N	S		S	A	C	K

PAGE 64

Hourglass

(1) samples, (2) psalms, (3) spasm, (4) mass, (5) mess, (6) seems, (7) sesame, (8) message

SANDWICH

FLASH

PAGE 65

Keep Going

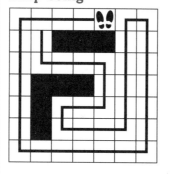

DELETE ONE

Delete A and find SHOPLIFTER

PAGE 66

Repeat Openers

H	U	L	A		A	T	L	A	S		S	C	A	N
E	R	I	N		T	I	A	R	A		A	C	R	E
A	A	R	D	W	O	L	V	E	S		T	S	A	R
P	L	E	I	A	D	E	S		H	E	R	A	L	D
			R	I	D				L	A	B			
S	H	O	O	T	S	U	P		D	E	P	A	R	T
T	O	O	N	S		G	R	A	V	E		T	E	E
A	S	P	S		B	L	O	N	D		C	H	A	P
R	E	S		G	U	I	L	T		V	O	I	C	E
S	L	A	T	E	R		E	S	C	A	L	A	T	E
			D	O	N				A	D	O			
S	O	A	P	E	D		I	L	L	I	N	O	I	S
E	R	I	E		E	E	C	U	M	M	I	N	G	S
M	A	S	K		E	T	A	I	L		Z	O	O	T
E	N	Y	A		P	A	N	S	Y		E	R	R	S

PAGE 67

BrainSnack®—Token Effort

On 10. In each set of 27 numbers—which are identical—the black token is always on the number under the red token + 3.

ONE LETTER LESS OR MORE

STRANGE

PAGE 68

Fruit

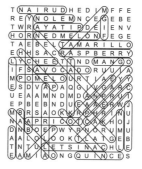

The difference between vegetables and fruit is vague and depends on how you look at things.

UNCANNY TURN

THE ARCTIC CIRCLE

PAGE 69

Santa Players

F	L	A	B		T	O	G	E	T		U	G	L	I
A	I	D	E		O	B	O	L	I		P	E	A	R
R	I	E	L		K	I	L	I	M		T	O	M	E
			D	O	L	E	D		A	D	O	R	E	D
P	A	J	A	M	A	S		C	L	I	N	G		
A	R	O	M	A	S		V	O	L	E		E	T	S
M	A	H	E	R		M	A	L	E	S		W	A	T
E	R	N	S		T	A	L	O	N		M	E	M	O
L	A	G		G	O	F	E	R		R	O	N	A	N
A	T	O		E	M	I	T		C	A	N	D	L	E
		O	M	A	H	A		D	E	M	O	T	E	D
F	E	D	O	R	A		G	R	A	S	P			
E	L	M	S		N	A	R	I	S		O	N	I	T
A	L	A	E		K	L	I	N	E		L	E	L	A
T	E	N	S		S	I	N	K	S		Y	E	L	P

PAGE 70

Number Cluster

1	2	2	3	3	4	4	4
8	8	8	8	8	8		4
6	6	6	1	8	8		5
6	2	5	5	5	5		5
6	2	4	4	4	5		6
6	3	3	3	4	7		6
7	7	7	7	7	7		7
Z	Z	Z	Z	Z	9	9	9

DOODLE PUZZLE

ShakeR

PAGE 71

BrainSnack®—Letter Logic

IS. All the other letters form pairs of two consecutive letters in the alphabet.

CONNECT TWO

SECOND BEST, TRUE STORY, UNINVITED GUEST, STUDY BREAK

PAGE 72

Holidays

D	I	O	R		A	G	O	R	A	S		B	L	T
O	L	I	O		B	L	U	I	S	H		A	A	H
C	O	L	U	M	B	U	S	D	A	Y		S	K	I
			L	I	E	G	E		P	L	A	T	E	N
S	E	V	E	N	S			O	B	I				
E	L	I	T	I	S	T	S		S	C	A	L	P	S
T	A	C	T	S		B	A	T	I	K		L	E	A
S	I	T	E		B	A	R	O	N		N	E	R	D
O	N	O		V	I	R	A	L		R	A	D	I	I
N	E	R	E	I	D		N	U	M	E	R	A	L	S
		I	T	S			E	N	C	Y	S	T		
F	R	A	C	A	S		G	E	N	I	I			
A	I	D		V	E	T	E	R	A	N	S	D	A	Y
K	E	A		I	R	O	N	I	C		S	A	L	E
E	L	Y		S	E	R	E	N	E		I	D	E	A

PAGE 73

Sport Maze

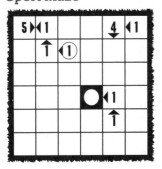

FRIENDS?

Each can have the suffix -AGE to form a new word.

PAGE 74

Word Sudoku

S	I	C	K	A	T	E	R	B
E	T	K	S	B	R	I	C	A
R	B	A	E	C	I	T	K	S
T	E	R	I	K	S	B	A	C
K	C	B	A	R	E	S	T	I
A	S	I	B	T	C	K	E	R
B	R	E	C	S	K	A	I	T
I	A	T	R	E	B	C	S	K
C	K	S	T	I	A	R	B	E

SANDWICH

STAND

PAGE 75

Yippee!

A	L	E	C		S	K	I	P	S		A	J	A	R
S	A	S	H		H	E	L	O	T		P	O	L	O
A	N	N	A	B	E	L	L	E	E		A	S	E	A
P	E	E	R	L	E	S	S		E	T	C	H	E	D
			G	A	T	O		E	L	I	H	U		
P	A	C	E	R	S		O	V	E	R	E	A	S	Y
O	C	H	R	E		A	W	A	R	E		T	E	A
L	U	I	S		M	I	N	D	S		B	R	A	C
A	T	M		R	A	R	E	E		T	E	E	T	H
R	E	P	A	I	R	E	D		F	I	N	E	S	T
		A	N	A	I	S		T	E	D	S			
T	A	N	G	L	E		T	H	E	A	T	E	R	S
H	A	Z	E		T	W	E	E	D	L	E	D	E	E
O	R	E	L		T	E	A	S	E		I	G	O	T
R	E	E	S		A	B	L	E	R		N	E	S	S

PAGE 76

Sudoku

3	5	1	9	7	8	6	2	4
2	8	7	6	3	4	1	9	5
4	6	9	5	1	2	3	7	8
8	4	3	2	9	6	5	1	7
5	7	2	1	8	3	9	4	6
1	9	6	4	5	7	8	3	2
7	3	5	8	4	9	2	6	1
9	2	8	7	6	1	4	5	3
6	1	4	3	2	5	7	8	9

DOUBLETALK

HEARD/HERD

PAGE 77

BrainSnack®—Alphabet

Letter K. All closed letters are blue and all open letters are yellow.

LETTERBLOCKS

JACKET
SWEATER

PAGE 78

Disney Filmfest

T	O	T	S		M	O	O	D	S		A	T	M	S
L	U	A	U		O	N	I	C	E		S	H	O	P
C	I	N	D	E	R	E	L	L	A		S	E	L	A
			A	V	E	R	Y		F	I	E	L	D	S
A	P	T	N	E	S	S		P	A	T	T	I		
M	Y	H	E	R	O		T	I	R	E	S	O	M	E
B	R	E	S	T		T	O	P	E	R		N	A	L
L	I	R	E		P	I	P	E	R		A	K	I	D
E	T	E		R	E	M	I	T		G	U	I	D	E
D	E	S	P	O	T	I	C		R	A	D	N	E	R
		C	A	S	E	D		M	A	L	I	G	N	S
L	A	U	P	E	R		A	I	S	L	E			
A	R	E	A		P	O	C	A	H	O	N	T	A	S
C	A	R	Y		A	D	I	M	E		C	E	N	T
E	L	S	A		N	A	D	I	R		E	D	D	Y

PAGE 79

Spot the Differences

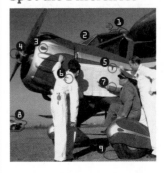

CHANGE ONE

GUNG HO

PAGE 80

Horoscope

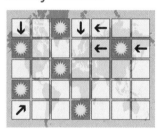

REPOSITION PREPOSITION

IN CASE OF

PAGE 81

Futoshiki

5	2	1	3	4
4	1	5	2	3
1	5	3 < 4	2
3	4	2	5	1
2 < 3	4 > 1	5

CONNECT TWO

AWFULLY GOOD, STEEL WOOL, WORKING HOLIDAY, YOUNG ADULT

PAGE 82

Advanced Geometry

C	O	S	T	A		B	E	E	P		A	H	A	B
A	S	C	O	T		A	R	A	L		S	O	N	Y
P	E	A	R	L		T	I	R	E		L	A	T	E
P	E	N	T	A	G	O	N	P	A	P	E	R	S	
		I	S	A	N			S	S	E				
F	A	B	L	E	S		T	R	A	I	P	S	E	S
O	P	A	L	S		R	A	I	N	S		C	L	I
N	A	N	A		B	U	I	L	T		W	R	I	T
D	R	J		K	R	I	L	L		S	O	U	S	A
U	T	O	P	I	A	N	S		C	O	M	B	E	R
		A	N	C		B	I	D	A					
	G	O	L	D	E	N	T	R	I	A	N	G	L	E
G	A	L	A		L	O	B	E		P	I	L	O	T
I	R	O	C		E	V	A	N		O	Z	O	N	E
L	Y	R	E		T	A	R	T		P	E	W	E	E

PAGE 83

Home, Garden and Kitchen

Garden tools are not precision equipment, but they must be robust and moisture-resistant.

SANDWICH

LAND

PAGE 84

Sunny Weather

UNCANNY TURN

INTRUSION

PAGE 85

Animated Films

S	M	U	G	•	O	W	N	E	R		S	K	E	W
A	O	N	E		R	H	I	N	O		T	U	N	E
O	P	E	N	S	E	A	S	O	N		A	N	N	A
			E	T	A	L		E	L	G	A	R		
O	F	F	S	I	D	E		S	H	E	L	F		
U	R	I	E	L		S	W	E	A	R		U	L	M
T	E	N	E	T	S		E	N	V	Y		P	I	E
P	E	D		P	L	A	T	O			A	N	T	
U	Z	I		O	L	A	V		C	O	R	N	E	T
T	E	N		B	A	S	E	S		P	E	D	A	L
	G	R	I	T	S		P	R	E	P	A	R	E	
D	O	N	U	T		E	E	R	O					
A	P	E	S		M	A	D	A	G	A	S	C	A	R
Y	A	M	S		M	A	O	R	I		E	A	S	Y
S	H	O	O		C	R	O	S	S		S	A	K	E

PAGE 86

BrainSnack®—Digital Display

4. Per column the sum of the two first numbers, multiplied by the third number always equals 20. $(2 + 3) \times 4 = (1 + 3) \times 5 = (5 + 5) \times 2 = (0 + 4) \times 5 = (1 + 4) \times 4 = 20$.

ONE LETTER LESS OR MORE

FRAGILE

PAGE 87

Kakuro

9	8	1		9	5	8	4
5	1			4	3		3	8
	3	2	9	7		1	2	9
8	6			6	2	5		
4	9	3	1		8	9	5	
		7	3	9	4		1	7
7	5	2		1	3	5		8
1	2		7	2		2	4	1
9	1		9	7		9	5	2

BLOCK ANAGRAM

INDEPENDENT

PAGE 88

Fictional Lawyers I

D	R	A	B		S	H	A	R	P		A	P	E	S
O	O	N	A		T	A	L	I	A		V	E	G	A
R	U	D	Y	B	A	Y	L	O	R		I	R	O	N
M	E	A	S	U	R	E	S		L	E	A	R	N	S
			T	R	E	K		N	A	T	T	Y		
I	S	L	A	N	D		C	O	N	T	E	M	P	T
W	A	I	T	S		J	U	I	C	E		A	R	A
A	L	O	E		C	U	R	S	E		A	S	I	S
S	O	N		A	R	N	I	E		S	M	O	C	K
A	N	E	C	D	O	T	E		T	H	A	N	E	S
		L	H	A	S	A		H	O	A	R			
O	T	H	E	R	S		O	U	T	L	I	N	E	S
M	O	U	E		B	E	N	M	A	T	L	O	C	K
O	R	T	S		A	R	E	A	L		L	O	R	I
O	O	Z	E		R	A	I	N	S		O	N	U	S

PAGE 89

Word Sudoku

S	D	L	B	N	R	A	J	K
B	A	K	J	D	S	L	R	N
J	R	N	K	A	L	S	D	B
A	L	B	D	S	J	K	N	R
D	N	R	L	B	K	J	S	A
K	J	S	N	R	A	B	L	D
R	B	J	S	K	D	N	A	L
N	S	A	R	L	B	D	K	J
L	K	D	A	J	N	R	B	S

DOUBLETALK
PLAIN/PLANE

PAGE 90

Keep Going

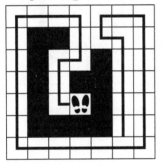

DELETE ONE
Delete S and find TANTRUM

PAGE 91

Fictional Lawyers II

P	A	C	E		I	D	L	E	R		S	A	N	A
I	R	O	N		N	O	O	N	E		W	R	E	N
P	A	T	T	Y	H	E	W	E	S		I	N	A	N
		R	E	A	R	S		I	G	N	I	T	E
B	E	F	A	L	L	S		A	D	A	G	E
U	N	R	I	P	E		D	U	E	T		B	A	R
S	C	A	N	S		B	E	R	N	E		E	L	O
K	I	N		C	A	R	A	T			C	B	S
I	N	K		W	H	I	R	L		T	A	K	E	I
N	A	G		E	E	L	Y		L	O	M	E	I	N
	A	C	R	E	S		D	E	P	O	R	T	S
P	A	L	L	E	T		D	O	G	I	E
E	N	V	Y		A	L	L	Y	M	C	B	E	A	L
E	N	I	D		H	A	I	L	E		A	N	D	Y
L	O	N	E		S	E	V	E	N		E	D	E	N

PAGE 92

Sport Maze

SANDWICH
ROOM

PAGE 93

Sudoku

2	1	6	7	3	8	4	9	5
5	9	3	6	4	1	7	2	8
8	7	4	5	9	2	3	1	6
6	3	1	8	7	4	9	5	2
7	2	9	3	5	6	1	8	4
4	8	5	2	1	9	6	7	3
1	6	2	4	8	7	5	3	9
3	4	7	9	2	5	8	6	1
9	5	8	1	6	3	2	4	7

CONNECT TWO
SAFE BET, BLIND EYE, BABY GRAND, MODERN HISTORY

PAGE 94

BrainSnack®—Full Piggy

Piggy bank D. All piggy banks with noses pointing to the right are full.

LETTERBLOCKS
CHERRY
BANANAS

PAGE 95

R&B Classics I

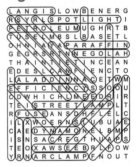

PAGE 96

Light

Low-energy lightbulbs last longer than incandescent ones, which means fewer bulbs are thrown out.

CHANGE ONE
PIPE DREAM

PAGE 97

BrainSnack®—Missing Middle

Nucleus 3. Squares can be made by joining nuclei of the same color as corner points of the squares.

DOODLE PUZZLE
GString

PAGE 98

R&B Classics II

O	K	R	A		A	N	A	M	E		O	P	T	S
P	E	A	R		N	U	T	T	Y		P	E	R	U
S	A	M	A	N	D	D	A	V	E		I	R	O	N
		B	A	R	E	D		T	R	A	C	T	S	
R	E	T	I	R	E	S		M	E	A	T	Y		
I	T	H	A	C	A		J	O	E	P	E	S	C	I
T	H	E	N	O		S	O	R	T	S		L	O	N
Z	A	P	S		F	I	L	T	H		C	E	N	T
E	N	E		B	A	T	T	Y		D	O	D	G	E
S	E	N	T	R	I	E	S		R	I	N	G	E	R
		G	O	A	T	S		E	A	S	T	E	R	N
C	H	U	R	C	H		A	L	I	C	E			
H	A	I	R		F	A	T	S	D	O	M	I	N	O
A	N	N	E		U	N	T	I	E		P	R	O	W
P	A	S	S		L	A	U	E	R		T	A	M	E

PAGE 99

Sudoku X

7	6	2	5	9	3	4	1	8
3	5	4	7	8	1	9	6	2
8	1	9	6	2	4	3	7	5
5	3	8	2	6	7	1	4	9
6	4	7	9	1	5	2	8	3
2	9	1	4	3	8	7	5	6
4	8	5	3	7	2	6	9	1
1	2	6	8	4	9	5	3	7
9	7	3	1	5	6	8	2	4

FRIENDS?

Each can have the prefix MONO- to form a new word.

PAGE 100

Binairo

I	O	I	O	I	I	O	O	I	O	O	I
O	I	O	I	O	I	O	I	O	I	O	I
O	O	I	I	O	O	I	I	O	I	I	O
I	I	O	O	I	I	O	O	I	O	O	I
O	O	I	I	O	O	I	O	I	O	I	I
O	I	I	O	O	I	O	I	O	I	I	O
I	O	O	I	I	O	I	O	O	I	O	I
I	I	O	O	I	O	I	O	I	O	I	O
O	O	I	I	O	I	O	I	I	O	I	O
O	O	I	O	I	O	I	I	O	I	O	I
I	I	O	I	O	O	I	O	I	I	O	O
I	I	O	O	I	I	O	I	O	O	I	O

UNCANNY TURN

THE NUDE IN ART

PAGE 101

Crazy Quilt

O	N	M	E		L	A	M	A	S		S	T	I	R
P	E	E	N		I	R	E	N	E		A	H	S	O
A	R	I	T	H	M	E	T	I	C		I	R	O	N
L	O	R	R	A	I	N	E		R	U	L	E	R	S
		A	L	T	A		G	E	N	O	A			
S	P	I	N	E	S		S	A	T	U	R	D	A	Y
N	A	N	C	Y		G	O	L	E	M		B	A	A
O	N	C	E		C	A	R	E	D		C	A	R	L
O	D	O		G	R	I	T	S		T	A	R	O	T
P	A	M	P	L	O	N	A		S	E	R	E	N	A
		P	R	E	S	S		R	I	T	E			
F	E	L	O	N	S		G	A	L	O	S	H	E	S
U	T	E	P		B	U	R	D	E	N	S	O	M	E
E	R	T	E		A	G	A	I	N		E	L	I	A
L	E	E	R		R	O	B	O	T		D	E	L	L

PAGE 102

Keep Going

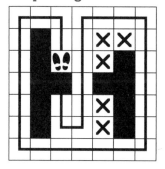

REPOSITION PREPOSITION

AS FAR AS

PAGE 103

BrainSnack®—Party Hardy

Party hat 5. All the other hats have just as many identically colored dots as ribbons, and one dot is the same color as the visor.

DOUBLETALK

ASSISTANTS/ASSISTANCE

PAGE 104

Eclectic Group

A	B	E	T		A	G	L	O	W		E	D	N	A
L	A	S	H		T	H	E	R	E		L	E	O	S
E	S	A	I		T	O	A	D	S		O	T	O	E
C	H	U	R	L	I	S	H		R	E	B	E	C	
			T	A	C	T		R	E	B	E	C		
L	O	S	E	R	S		C	H	R	I	S	T	E	N
O	P	T	E	D		I	R	E	N	E		I	L	E
G	R	A	N		K	N	O	T	S		A	V	E	R
I	A	L		G	I	A	N	T		A	M	E	N	D
C	H	E	Y	E	N	N	E		T	H	E	S	I	S
		M	A	R	G	E		B	E	A	R			
S	P	A	C	E	K		J	O	E	B	I	D	E	N
O	A	T	H		O	D	I	U	M		C	I	T	Y
F	R	E	T		N	O	B	L	E		A	N	T	E
T	E	S	S		G	R	E	E	D		N	E	A	T

PAGE 105

Sport Maze

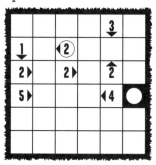

CONNECT TWO

SIT UP, CLIMB DOWN, CONSTANT CHANGE, SIGHT UNSEEN

PAGE 106

Sudoku X

1	3	9	7	8	4	5	6	2
4	5	2	6	9	3	7	1	8
6	7	8	1	2	5	4	9	3
7	2	4	9	1	8	6	3	5
8	9	5	2	3	6	1	7	4
3	1	6	5	4	7	8	2	9
5	4	7	3	6	9	2	8	1
2	6	3	8	5	1	9	4	7
9	8	1	4	7	2	3	5	6

SANDWICH

BONE

PAGE 107

A Night at the Opera

L	A	M	B		S	L	A	T		L	E	M	A	T
O	L	E	O		H	A	I	R		E	L	A	T	E
R	I	G	O	L	E	T	T	O		G	A	G	E	S
D	I	S	T	O	R	T		D	A	I	S	I	E	S
			L	I	R	E			R	O	T	C		
C	E	L	E	R	Y		J	E	N	N	I	F	E	R
O	S	A	G	E		H	A	R	I		C	L	I	O
O	T	T		C	A	D	R	E			U	D	O	
L	O	R	E		E	V	E	S		M	O	T	E	T
S	P	A	N	G	L	E	D		C	O	V	E	R	S
		V	A	L	E		A	R	I	E				
A	L	I	B	A	B	A		N	A	R	R	A	T	E
G	O	A	L	S		D	O	N	C	A	R	L	O	S
A	N	T	E	S		A	M	O	K		U	T	E	S
R	E	A	D	Y		R	A	Y	S		N	O	D	E

PAGE 108

BrainSnack®—Latin Rhythm

Maraca 5. On all other maracas the colored rings on the upper and lower halves follow the same order.

BLOCK ANAGRAM

CANDIDATES

PAGE 109

Word Pyramid

A, (1) at, (2) cat, (3) chat, (4) cheat, (5) chalet, (6) ethical, (7) athletic

DELETE ONE

Delete S and find RETRACTION

PAGE 110

Sunny Weather

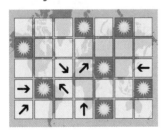

ONE LETTER LESS OR MORE

CALIBRATE

PAGE 111

Themeless

L	A	P	D		A	R	E	A	S		S	T	A	T
I	R	A	E		N	U	D	G	E		H	E	R	R
S	U	C	C	E	S	S	I	O	N		E	N	N	A
A	N	T	I	D	O	T	E		S	E	L	D	O	M
			M	I	N	I		C	A	R	V	E		
S	A	D	A	T		C	H	A	T	T	E	R	E	D
T	S	E	T	S	E		E	R	I	E		L	V	I
A	I	D	E		N	A	R	D	O		S	O	A	R
I	D	I		A	G	R	O		N	A	M	I	N	G
R	E	C	I	P	I	E	N	T		D	E	N	S	E
	A	D	A	N	O		R	I	A	L				
R	E	T	I	R	E		B	A	S	I	L	I	C	A
O	L	I	O		E	L	E	C	T	R	I	C	A	L
B	L	O	C		R	E	B	E	L		N	A	P	A
E	E	N	Y		S	W	E	D	E		G	L	E	N

PAGE 112

Sudoku Twin

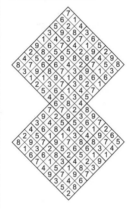

CHANGE ONE

DOUBLE TAKE

PAGE 113

Futoshiki

2	5	4	1	3
1	4 > 3	2	5
3	1	2	5	4
5	3	1	4	2
4	2	5	3 > 1

SANDWICH

CHECK

PAGE 114

Mixed Bag

S	N	A	P		S	C	U	L	L		S	P	O	T
H	I	L	O		C	A	R	E	Y		T	E	L	A
A	D	M	I	R	A	T	I	O	N		E	R	A	T
W	E	S	T	E	R	N	S		C	L	I	F	F	S
			I	T	E	A		S	H	O	N	E		
I	N	G	E	R		P	R	O	B	O	S	C	I	S
S	O	R	R	O	W		A	R	U	N		T	N	T
A	R	E	S		A	S	N	E	R		S	I	T	E
A	M	A		S	L	A	T		G	A	L	O	R	E
C	A	T	A	C	L	Y	S	M		F	I	N	A	L
	W	R	A	P	S		A	L	O	T				
A	T	H	E	N	A		B	R	O	U	H	A	H	A
B	A	I	T		P	R	I	V	I	L	E	G	E	S
B	O	T	H		E	E	L	E	R		R	E	A	P
A	S	E	A		R	O	L	L	E		S	S	T	S

PAGE 115

BrainSnack®—Color Me Up

Square 9. Orange comes from above, blue from the right, purple from the left and yellow from below.

CONNECT TWO

NEW IMPROVED, ALMOST DONE, GRADUATE STUDENT, INTIMATE STRANGERS

PAGE 116

Concentration—Translation

$60 = 六十$ $十一 = 11$
$76 = 七十六$ $三十八 = 38$
$99 = 九十九$ $五十八 = 58$

UNCANNY TURN

A SENTENCE OF DEATH

PAGE 117

Sci-Fi Writers

T	A	P	A	S		E	R	I	C		M	I	N	D
E	R	E	C	T		V	I	T	O		A	S	E	A
L	A	R	R	Y	N	I	V	E	N		T	A	R	T
			E	M	I	L	E		T	I	R	A	D	E
S	T	R	A	I	T	S		B	A	S	I	C		
O	S	A	G	E	S		C	O	I	L		A	R	P
O	H	Y	E	S		R	H	O	N	E		S	E	E
N	I	B	S		P	E	L	T	S		D	I	G	S
A	R	R		H	O	B	O	S		R	E	M	I	T
S	T	A		E	P	E	E		B	E	C	O	M	E
		D	O	R	I	C		P	A	L	A	V	E	R
C	O	B	U	R	N		F	E	T	I	D			
E	M	U	S		J	U	L	E	S	V	E	R	N	E
S	O	R	T		A	S	A	P		E	N	U	R	E
T	O	Y	S		Y	A	M	S		S	T	E	A	L

PAGE 118

Keep Going

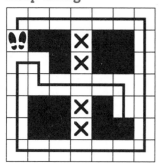

FRIENDS?

Each can have the prefix HYPER- to form a new word.

PAGE 119

Wine

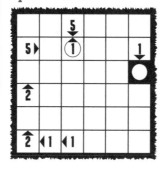

Phylloxera destroyed hundreds of vineyards in Europe, only American grapevines were resistant.

LETTERBLOCKS

RESPECT
REVENGE

PAGE 120

Movie Villains

C	O	S	T		N	I	N	E	S		A	D	A	M
H	A	L	O		I	N	E	R	T		V	A	L	E
A	T	O	M		C	R	A	N	E		A	R	E	A
T	H	E	J	O	K	E	R		P	O	T	T	E	D
		O	D	E				R	A	H				
M	A	G	N	O	L	I	A		F	E	R	V	O	R
A	M	E	E	R		D	R	U	G	S		A	R	A
P	A	N	S		W	E	I	G	H		E	D	I	T
L	I	E		E	A	S	E	L		S	L	E	E	T
E	N	R	A	P	T		S	I	S	T	E	R	L	Y
		A	L	E				A	I	M				
B	E	L	I	E	F		M	R	F	R	E	E	Z	E
R	A	Z	E		A	U	R	A	E		N	C	O	S
A	R	O	N		S	N	E	R	T		T	R	O	T
E	N	D	S		T	O	D	A	Y		S	U	M	O

PAGE 121

Sport Maze

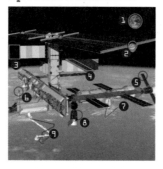

DOUBLETALK

CHORD/CORD

PAGE 122

Classic Cinema

P	O	R	T		A	S	H	E	R		K	A	L	E
A	P	E	R		S	T	E	V	E		A	B	I	E
S	A	T	O		T	Y	R	E	S		T	E	A	L
T	H	E	M	A	R	X	B	R	O	T	H	E	R	S
		B	R	A			U	R	I					
H	O	M	O	N	Y	M		F	R	E	E	D	O	M
U	R	A	N	O		E	L	E	C	T		R	P	I
M	O	V	E		S	L	A	T	E		D	O	I	T
I	N	E		L	A	T	T	E		L	E	O	N	E
D	O	N	K	E	Y	S		S	M	A	L	L	E	R
		E	S	O			A	R	I					
L	A	U	R	E	N	C	E	O	L	I	V	I	E	R
E	A	R	N		A	H	A	R	D		E	L	S	E
E	R	S	E		R	A	R	E	E		R	I	T	A
S	E	A	L		A	N	S	O	N		Y	E	A	R

PAGE 123

Spot the Differences

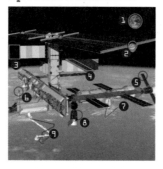

BLOCK ANAGRAM

CONVENTION

PAGE 124

Sudoku

6	8	7	3	5	2	9	4	1
4	3	1	8	9	6	2	5	7
2	5	9	7	1	4	8	3	6
8	4	3	6	7	5	1	9	2
9	1	2	4	8	3	6	7	5
7	6	5	1	2	9	3	8	4
3	2	6	9	4	7	5	1	8
5	7	8	2	3	1	4	6	9
1	9	4	5	6	8	7	2	3

ONE LETTER LESS OR MORE

AMERICANS

PAGE 125

Word Sudoku

E	I	W	K	T	N	X	R	O
N	X	O	W	I	R	E	K	T
K	R	T	X	E	O	W	N	I
I	N	K	O	X	E	T	W	R
O	T	X	I	R	W	N	E	K
W	E	R	N	K	T	O	I	X
T	O	N	R	W	K	I	X	E
X	K	E	T	N	I	R	O	W
R	W	I	E	O	X	K	T	N

DOODLE PUZZLE

DesPair

PAGE 126

BrainSnack®—Mirror, Mirror

Opening 3. The perspective of the side walls is drawn incorrectly.

END GAME

T E N D O N S
R E N D E R S
U N E N D E D
E X T E N D S

PAGE 127

Antonyms

A	S	T	A		L	A	U	G	H		S	S	G	B
G	L	U	G		E	N	N	U	I		E	T	A	L
R	O	T	E		G	O	I	N	G		A	R	I	E
A	B	U	N	D	A	N	T		H	E	R	A	L	D
	C	O	T						L	E	I		
T	R	A	I	N	E	E	S		B	U	D	G	E	D
R	A	C	E	S		S	P	I	E	L		H	M	O
A	R	C	S		S	P	I	C	Y		A	T	O	Z
S	E	I		J	O	Y	C	E		C	R	E	T	E
H	E	D	G	E	S		A	S	S	I	G	N	E	D
	E	R	S					U	N	U				
T	E	N	E	T	S		R	E	M	E	M	B	E	R
A	N	T	E		I	B	E	A	M		E	L	L	A
T	O	A	D		L	O	O	S	E		N	E	A	T
A	L	L	Y		L	O	S	E	R		T	U	N	E

PAGE 128

Hourglass

(1) tsunami, (2) Austin,
(3) aunts, (4) tuna, (5) turn,
(6) burnt, (7) bunter,
(8) tribune

MISSING LETTER MOTTO

TRUTH AND VIRTUE (various universities)

PAGE 129

Horoscope

END GAME

P R E T E N D
E X P E N D S
S L E N D E R
T E N D E R S

PAGE 130

Mishmash

T	A	R	O		S	C	O	T	T		P	S	I	S
A	R	A	B		C	O	P	R	A		R	I	D	E
L	E	S	S	E	R	B	E	A	R		A	X	L	E
C	A	P	E	T	O	W	N		P	I	N	T	E	R
	S	A	D	E		R	A	N	C	H				
C	L	A	S	P		B	E	A	U	G	E	S	T	E
R	E	D	E	E	M		L	I	L	A		E	E	R
A	P	O	D		I	R	A	N	I		A	N	N	A
M	E	L		G	N	A	T		N	O	I	S	E	S
P	R	E	V	E	N	T	E	D		A	R	E	T	E
	S	I	T	E	S		R	O	T	C				
R	E	C	E	S	S		M	A	V	E	R	I	C	K
O	V	E	N		O	R	I	G	I	N	A	L	L	Y
S	I	N	N		T	A	L	O	N		F	E	E	L
A	L	T	A		A	L	O	N	E		T	A	M	E

PAGE 131

Energy

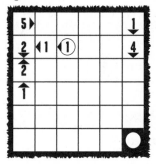

According to the law of conservation of energy, the total amount of energy in an isolated system remains constant over time.

UNCANNY TURN

THE SOPRANO SINGER

PAGE 132

Binairo

1	1	0	0	1	0	1	1	0	1	0
0	1	1	0	1	0	1	0	1	1	0	1	0
1	0	1	1	0	1	0	0	0	1	0	1
1	0	0	1	0	0	1	1	0	1	1
0	1	1	0	1	1	0	0	1	1	0
0	0	1	0	1	1	0	1	1	0	1
1	1	0	1	0	0	1	0	0	1	1
1	1	0	1	0	1	1	0	1	0	0
0	0	1	0	1	1	0	1	0	1	1
1	1	0	1	1	0	1	0	1	0	0
0	0	1	1	0	1	0	1	0	1	1

DOUBLETALK

MISSED/MIST

PAGE 133

La Scala Title Roles

S	W	A	P		S	E	N	O	R		C	A	T	E
A	R	I	L		E	M	O	T	E		A	L	A	N
M	A	D	A	M	E	B	U	T	T	E	R	F	L	Y
S	P	E	C	I	M	E	N		A	L	P	A	C	A
	A	X	E	D		S	I	D	E					
S	T	A	T	E	D		T	E	L	E	T	H	O	N
U	R	G	E	S		R	O	V	E	R		A	C	E
R	E	N	D		C	A	P	E	R		C	I	T	E
A	V	E		R	O	D	I	N		N	O	T	E	D
H	I	S	P	A	N	I	C		L	E	V	I	T	Y
	H	I	F	I		A	A	G	E					
A	R	I	O	S	O		A	S	T	E	R	I	S	K
B	A	R	B	E	R	O	F	S	E	V	I	L	L	E
A	M	O	I		M	O	R	E	L		N	E	O	N
S	A	N	A		S	O	O	T	Y		G	A	T	O

PAGE 134

Sport Maze

5▶				↓
2↓	◀1	①		↓4
2↓				
1↑				
				●

LETTER LINE

BANDLEADER; BLADDER; ENABLED; LEARNED; LANDED

PAGE 135

Kakuro

1	2	6		5	2		9	1
9	8		7	8	6		1	4
4	5	3	9		7	5		3
5		4			3	1	5	
	8	1	2		1	6	3	
6	4		3	5	7		8	9
7	2	9		9	2	6		6
5		2		1		8	5	7
3	6	7		7	5	4	8	

LETTERBLOCKS

HOSTING
NETWORK

PAGE 136

Here Comes the Judge

T	R	A	P		S	H	A	S	T	A		P	R	O	
E	I	R	E		P	O	L	L	E	D		A	I	R	
S	L	Y	S	T	A	L	L	O	N	E		U	L	M	
T	E	E	T	E	R	S				L	I	L	L	E	
			E	A	S	T		C	A	I	R	N			
P	I	E	R	R	E		B	L	A	N	K	E	T	S	
H	O	L	E	S		B	L	A	R	E		W	O	K	
A	W	E	D		T	E	A	S	E		A	M	O	I	
S	A	N		B	A	R	N	S		P	L	A	N	T	
E	N	A	M	O	R	E	D		P	L	A	N	E	S	
	K	A	R	A	T		H	A	A	S					
B	E	A	R	D			A	U	S	T	R	I	A		
R	A	G		E	L	I	H	U	S	M	A	I	L	S	
E	V	A		R	E	C	I	T	E		I	T	S	A	
D	E	N		S	E	E	M	E	D		R	E	A	P	

PAGE 137

BrainSnack®—Lost Cube

On base 7. Cubes on each level and each vertical column have their own particular color.

DOODLE PUZZLE

WallStreet

PAGE 138

Word Sudoku

I	Z	E	J	T	Y	V	U	N
V	N	Y	I	Z	U	J	E	T
U	J	T	E	N	V	Z	Y	I
Z	I	J	U	Y	N	E	T	V
Y	T	N	V	I	E	U	J	Z
E	V	U	Z	J	T	N	I	Y
J	Y	V	T	E	Z	I	N	U
N	E	Z	Y	U	I	T	V	J
T	U	I	N	V	J	Y	Z	E

CHANGE ONE

BLUE RIBBON

PAGE 139

BrainSnack®—Missing Number

17. Every number equals the number of differently colored cubes. There are a total of 17 cubes that are not white.

END GAME

F R I E N D S
G O D S E N D
S P E N D E R
S E N D O F F

PAGE 140

Themeless

L	U	M	P		S	E	O	U	L		S	E	L	A
A	L	A	R		E	X	T	R	A		T	R	I	P
I	N	V	E	N	T	I	O	N	S		R	I	M	E
C	A	S	S	E	T	T	E		P	I	E	C	E	S
			E	V	O	E		A	A	R	E			
A	L	I	N	E		D	E	F	L	A	T	I	O	N
D	E	S	C	R	Y		D	A	M	N		R	N	A
D	O	L	E		O	P	E	R	A		T	E	E	M
E	N	E		T	U	R	N		S	P	O	N	G	E
D	I	S	H	O	N	E	S	T		A	R	E	A	S
		O	R	G	Y		H	A	L	E				
T	R	I	B	E	S		R	E	L	I	A	B	L	E
E	A	R	N		T	R	E	M	E	N	D	O	U	S
S	U	M	O		E	I	D	E	R		O	N	I	T
S	L	A	B		R	O	O	S	T		R	O	S	A

PAGE 141

Sudoku X

4	6	2	9	7	1	3	8	5
5	8	9	3	4	6	7	2	1
7	1	3	5	2	8	6	9	4
8	9	7	1	6	4	2	5	3
6	2	5	7	9	3	4	1	8
1	3	4	8	5	2	9	7	6
9	4	1	6	8	7	5	3	2
2	7	8	4	3	5	1	6	9
3	5	6	2	1	9	8	4	7

CHANGELINGS

S A B B A T I C A L
B L A C K B O A R D
U N I V E R S I T Y

PAGE 142

Safe Code

$$\frac{51}{49} \begin{vmatrix} 38 \\ 62 \end{vmatrix} \begin{vmatrix} 23 \\ 77 \end{vmatrix} = 100$$

$$+ \quad + \quad +$$

BLOCK ANAGRAM

PRESIDENT

PAGE 143

Elementary School

C	H	U	M		M	O	T	E	T		S	L	I	T
L	A	N	E		A	G	O	R	A		T	I	R	E
A	U	S	T	A	N	D	A	R	D		O	B	O	E
S	T	E	A	D	I	E	D		P	O	L	A	N	D
P	E	R	L	M	A	N		C	O	V	E	T		
			L	A	C		T	A	L	E	N	T	E	D
E	L	F	I	N		S	A	B	E	R		E	R	E
M	A	R	C		J	A	P	E	S		P	R	I	M
I	C	E		L	U	G	E	R		S	A	Y	S	O
R	E	D	E	E	M	E	R		B	A	N			
		D	R	I	B	S		P	I	R	A	N	H	A
A	R	I	O	S	O		L	E	G	A	C	I	E	S
S	U	E	D		J	A	Y	A	G	H	E	E	L	S
A	S	H	E		E	C	O	L	I		A	C	M	E
P	E	G	S		T	E	N	S	E		N	E	S	T

PAGE 144

Keep Going

REPOSITON PREPOSITION

IN FRONT OF

PAGE 145

Word Ladder

cape, page, game, meal, mule, blue; bingo, begin, bring, brain, cabin, bacon, ocean

DOUBLETALK

WAIT/WEIGHT

PAGE 146

Latin 101

L	A	P	D		B	R	I	E	F		L	E	A	F
E	S	A	I		L	I	M	B	O		E	L	U	L
A	S	I	S		O	T	A	R	U		T	I	N	E
P	E	R	S	O	N	A	N	O	N	G	R	A	T	A
		O	I	D			T	A	I					
C	H	E	L	S	E	A		S	A	M	P	R	A	S
L	E	A	V	E		U	N	T	I	E		E	R	E
E	I	R	E		A	D	O	R	N		A	B	E	D
A	N	E		A	L	I	B	I		E	L	E	N	A
R	E	D	H	E	A	T		A	F	R	I	C	A	N
			E	R	R				E	N	E			
N	O	N	C	O	M	P	O	S	M	E	N	T	I	S
A	M	O	K		I	L	O	N	A		A	R	T	Y
S	O	U	L		N	E	P	A	L		T	E	E	N
H	O	N	E		G	A	S	P	E		E	S	M	E

PAGE 147

BrainSnack®—Pricey Painting

51031. Every color stands for the following: a black square = 10,000; red = 1,000; green = 100; blue = 10; purple = 1 and white = 0.

DOODLE PUZZLE

AirBag

PAGE 148

Word Wheel

amp, cap, cop, map, mop, nap, nip, pan, pic, pin, camp, coop, pain, pion, panic, piano, pinon, companion.

UNCANNY TURN

PRODUCE

PAGE 149

Melange

A	V	E	C		C	L	A	N	G		L	E	A	D
L	E	V	I		A	E	R	I	E		A	F	R	O
F	I	O	R	E	N	T	I	N	O		U	F	O	S
A	N	E	C	D	O	T	E		M	A	R	I	N	O
		L	E	E	S		R	E	B	E	C			
B	A	S	I	N	S		B	O	T	A	N	I	S	T
A	L	A	N	S		D	O	O	R	S		E	T	A
S	A	N	G		P	A	R	T	Y		G	N	A	T
I	M	A		G	E	N	E	S		D	I	C	T	A
C	O	N	C	E	D	E	D		P	R	A	Y	E	R
		T	A	L	E	S		L	O	O	M			
S	N	O	R	T	S		S	A	L	V	A	G	E	D
T	E	N	T		T	A	T	T	L	E	T	A	L	E
E	R	I	E		A	G	A	T	E		T	R	I	N
P	O	O	R		L	O	R	E	N		I	B	E	T

PAGE 150

Sport Maze

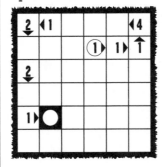

DELETE ONE

Delete S and find IDEAL

PAGE 151

Word Sudoku

W	P	M	C	R	L	N	A	E
R	A	N	E	W	M	L	C	P
E	C	L	P	A	N	W	R	M
A	M	P	L	C	E	R	N	W
N	L	E	R	P	W	C	M	A
C	W	R	N	M	A	E	P	L
M	E	C	A	L	R	P	W	N
L	R	A	W	N	P	M	E	C
P	N	W	M	E	C	A	L	R

ONE LETTER LESS OR MORE

ANSWERING

PAGE 152

Spot the Differences

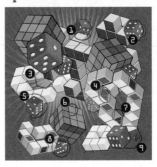

FRIENDS?

Each can have the suffix -ISM to form a new word.

PAGE 153

Variety Pack

B	E	R	N		H	A	D	E	S		D	A	T	A
A	L	A	I		A	R	O	M	A		E	L	A	N
K	I	N	G	A	R	T	H	U	R		C	A	P	O
E	S	T	H	E	R	S		S	A	H	A	R	A	N
			T	R	I				N	O	M			
P	R	E	C	I	S	E		A	D	A	P	T	E	D
A	I	D	A		R	O	T	O	R		H	M	O	
S	T	E	P	H	E	N	S	O	N	D	H	E	I	M
T	E	N		A	N	S	O	N		E	R	L	E	
A	S	S	A	U	L	T		E	N	T	R	E	E	S
			P	T	A				O	O	O			
V	E	S	P	E	R	S		M	I	N	I	M	U	M
E	V	I	L		G	A	R	Y	S	I	N	I	S	E
R	E	N	E		E	N	U	R	E		E	L	E	A
B	R	E	T		D	E	G	A	S		S	O	R	T

PAGE 154

BrainSnack®—Tick Tock

Clock B 3 o'clock. 2 hours difference with A and D, and C and E are running fast in the afternoon.

CHANGE ONE

WATCH OUT

PAGE 155

Basketball

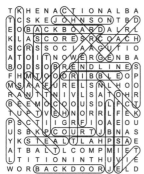

The National Basketball Association, or NBA for short, is the most prestigious basketball competition in the world.

LETTERBLOCKS

AIRPORT
LUGGAGE

PAGE 156

Themeless

F	E	T	A		S	P	A	S	M		I	M	A	M
A	T	O	P		C	I	L	I	A		N	O	M	E
S	U	P	P	O	R	T	I	N	G		D	U	P	E
T	I	E	R	N	E	Y		E	A	S	I	E	S	T
			O	D	E				Z	A	G			
N	I	R	V	A	N	A		R	I	P	O	S	T	E
A	R	E	A		B	E	A	N	O			E	W	E
S	E	A	L	Y	H	A	M	T	E	R	R	I	E	R
A	N	C		O	A	S	E	S			O	N	E	I
L	E	T	T	U	C	E		O	B	S	C	E	N	E
			U	N	I			A	S	K				
A	V	E	N	G	E	D		A	R	T	E	M	I	S
L	I	E	N		N	I	G	H	T	S	T	I	C	K
M	E	R	E		D	O	U	S	E		E	L	O	I
A	W	O	L		A	R	M	O	R		D	E	N	T

PAGE 157

BrainSnack®—The Sky's the Limit

Skyscraper 2. The number of lights should equal the number of floors.

DOODLE PUZZLE

MosCow

PAGE 158

Illnesses

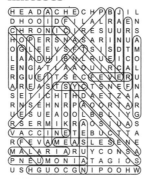

Childhood illnesses are viral diseases that are not usually serious but are very contagious.

DOUBLETALK

WASTE/WAIST

PAGE 159

Do the Math

S	L	A	V		P	E	T	A	L		M	O	A	T
R	U	B	E		E	D	E	N	S		A	A	G	E
O	N	E	H	U	N	D	R	E	D	T	H	R	E	E
S	A	L	E	S	M	A	N		O	L	S	E	N	
			M	E	A			O	W	E				
I	N	T	E	R	N	A	L		M	A	R	C	U	S
N	E	O	N		L	I	V	E	R		L	S	U	
T	W	O	T	H	O	U	S	A	N	D	F	O	U	R
R	E	T		A	L	I	A	S		O	V	A	L	
A	R	S	E	N	E		S	E	V	E	R	E	L	Y
			U	D	O			A	R	T				
S	W	I	R	L		S	A	N	G	U	I	N	E	
T	H	R	E	E	M	I	L	L	I	O	N	S	I	X
B	O	O	K		A	N	A	I	S		E	N	N	A
D	A	N	A		D	E	P	T	H		S	T	E	M

PAGE 160

Sudoku Twin

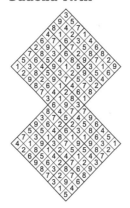

LETTER LINE

WILDERNESS; WINDLESS; SWINDLES; RENEWS; RINSE

PAGE 161

Keep Going

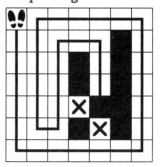

REPOSITION PREPOSITION

FAR FROM

PAGE 162

Do More Math

R	A	N	T		S	P	O	O	F		A	C	M	E
A	L	O	E		E	R	R	O	R		S	H	I	N
S	E	V	E	N	T	Y	T	H	O	U	S	A	N	D
P	E	A	N	U	T		U	N	I	T	E	S		
			I	D	E	M		E	F	T	S			
M	A	D	E	I	R	A		T	R	O	T	O	U	T
A	M	U	S	T		D	E	C	O			A	V	E
F	O	R	T	Y	O	N	E	H	U	N	D	R	E	D
I	O	S			P	E	R	E		O	R	E	A	D
A	N	T	A	R	E	S		R	A	B	I	D	L	Y
			B	A	R	S		S	L	A	V			
U	N	L	A	C	E			B	L	E	A	R	S	
S	I	X	T	Y	T	W	O	M	I	L	L	I	O	N
E	L	I	E		T	A	L	O	N		E	D	D	A
R	E	I	D		A	D	D	T	O		D	E	E	P

PAGE 163

Monkey Business

1) *War Horse*
2) *Curious George and the Pizza*
3) *Diary of a Wimpy Kid*
4) *Puff the Magic Dragon*
5) *Fire and Ice*

BLOCK ANAGRAM

NOMINATION

PAGE 164

Clothing

For some men the tie is an essential piece of clothing that they put a lot of time and care into.

SUBTLY

PAGE 165

Full Name Please

S	H	A	Q		B	A	C	K	S		H	E	R	A
O	A	H	U		I	C	A	N	T		O	V	E	R
A	L	A	E		T	H	R	E	E		L	E	T	O
R	O	B	E	R	T	E	D	W	A	R	D	L	E	E
			N	E	E				L	O	U			
B	A	R	B	A	R	A		S	T	O	P	P	E	R
A	R	E	E	L		B	L	A	H	S		R	C	A
R	O	B	E		P	U	S	H	Y		S	O	O	N
O	N	E		P	A	T	T	I		S	K	U	L	K
N	I	C	H	O	L	S		B	E	T	I	D	E	S
			I	P	O				N	O	R			
W	I	L	L	I	A	M	H	A	L	L	M	A	C	Y
A	B	E	L		L	E	O	N	I		I	L	I	A
F	I	N	E		T	A	R	T	S		S	T	A	R
T	S	A	R		O	N	S	E	T		H	O	O	D

PAGE 166

Sunny Weather

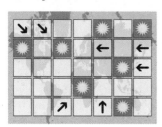

HOUSEMAID

PAGE 167

Concentration—Squared

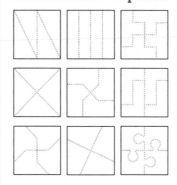

JUST DANCE

PAGE 168

Quote Unquote

C	A	L	M		S	H	O	E	D		T	W	I	G
A	R	O	E		L	A	N	A	I		H	O	T	E
W	I	L	L	R	O	G	E	R	S		R	O	S	E
S	A	L	V	A	G	E	S		G	L	A	D	Y	S
			I	R	A	N		D	R	I	L	Y		
S	T	O	L	E	N		H	E	A	D	L	A	N	D
A	I	S	L	E		F	A	L	C	O		L	O	A
R	A	C	E		E	L	S	I	E		P	L	O	T
E	R	A		H	Y	E	N	A		R	E	E	S	E
E	A	R	L	I	E	S	T		B	A	N	N	E	R
		W	O	R	T	H		P	A	L	E			
A	V	I	A	T	E		A	I	R	P	L	A	N	E
W	E	L	D		E	I	S	E	N	H	O	W	E	R
L	A	D	E		T	R	A	C	E		P	O	T	S
S	L	E	D		H	A	Y	E	S		E	L	S	E

PAGE 169

The Puzzled Librarian

1) *The Girl With the Dragon Tattoo*
2) *The Confession*
3) *The Bourne Betrayal*
4) *The Friday Night Knitting Club*
5) *Love the One You're With*
6) *The Lost Symbol*
7) *Under the Dome*
8) *The Eagle Has Landed*
9) *The Ginger Man*
10) *The Thorn Birds*

B U T T O N H O L E
H A L T E R N E C K
P I N S T R I P E S

PAGE 170

Elton John

The name Elton John is a combination of Elton Dean and Long John Baldry, two colleagues from his first group.

Delete S and find HUSTLER

PAGE 171

Futoshiki

2	3	4	5	1
1	4 > 3	2	5
	^	v		v
4	5	2 > 1	3
3	1	5 > 4	2
	^			
5	2	1	3 < 4

TennEssEe

PAGE 172

Word Pyramid

G, (1) e.g., (2) get, (3) gate, (4) agent, (5) eating, (6) vintage, (7) navigate

ENGLISH
SPANISH

PAGE 173

BrainSnack®—Directions

You will be back in starting position after signpost 10.

CHANGE ONE

DEAR SIR

PAGE 174

Celebrity Perfumes

D	A	L	Y		A	S	I	A		M	A	T	T	E
O	L	E	O		S	A	R	I		O	H	A	R	A
H	E	I	D	I	K	L	U	M		M	A	Y	O	R
			E	V	I	A	N		M	E	R	L	I	N
E	N	G	L	A	N	D		C	O	N	D	O		
R	O	W	E	N		S	C	A	N	T		R	I	B
O	P	E	R	A	S		A	R	T	S		S	C	I
I	A	N		E	A	R	T	H		W	I	T		
C	I	S		U	N	D	O		S	T	R	I	C	T
A	N	T		S	T	I	L	T		R	I	F	L	E
		E	V	E	R	T		S	H	A	T	T	E	R
S	A	F	E	L	Y		L	E	A	P	T			
I	M	A	G	E		K	A	T	Y	P	E	R	R	Y
N	A	N	A	S		E	L	S	E		R	H	E	A
G	R	I	N	S		G	O	E	S		S	O	A	K

ANSWERS TO QUICK AND DO YOU KNOW

p 15: Bay of Fundy
p 17: Robert Oppenheimer
p 19: Ian McKellen
p 21: *Chattanooga Choo Choo*
p 23: The League of Nations
p 25: Jimmy Durante
p 27: Canada at 56,453 miles (90,850 kilometers) or around 15 percent of the world's 372,384 miles (599,293 kilometers) of coastlines
p 29: Pablo Picasso
p 31: Agatha Christie
p 33: Geronimo
p 35: 22
p 37: Explorer 1
p 39: Gold
p 41: F.W. Woolworth
p 43: Johann Gutenberg
p 45: Sonny Liston
p 47: Peritonitis
p 49: Buffalo Bill
p 51: Jean Harlow
p 53: George Frederic Handel
p 55: Sweden (Kiki Haakonson)
p 57: Madame Tussaud
p 59: Douglas Fairbanks
p 61: D.W. Griffith, Charles Chaplin, Mary Pickford and Douglas Fairbanks
p 63: Prague, Czech Republic
p 65: Valentina Tereshkova
p 67: Shirley Temple
p 69: *Black Beauty*
p 71: Up to 55 miles (89 kilometres) per hour
p 73: A siege
p 75: International Committee of the Red Cross
p 77: Lawrence of Arabia
p 79: The "unexpected" opening of Tower Bridge
p 81: East River
p 83: Asmara
p 85: Simon Wiesenthal
p 87: Roald Amundsen (1911)
p 89: Louis Bleriot (1909)
p 91: Sneakers
p 93: To lift the foot from the burning sand
p 95: Rabat
p 97: Piano
p 99: A young innovator, Sam Foster, who convinced the Woolworth's store on the Atlantic City Boardwalk to sell his new brand of sunglasses—FosterGrant
p 101: Taj Mahal
p 103: A type of sail
p 105: Dublin
p 107: Beethoven's 5th
p 109: James Joyce
p 111: Raymond Chandler
p 113: Humphrey Bogart
p 115: 4
p 117: Anne
p 119: Clement Attlee
p 121: Theodore Roosevelt (Panama visit, 1906)
p 123: May Sutton (1905)
p 125: Truck driver
p 127: Canada
p 129: Northern Africa's Sahara, reaches temperatures of up to 122 degrees Fahrenheit (50 degrees Celsius) during the day
p 131: Edmund Barton
p 133: Zugspitze (9,718 feet/2,962 meters)
p 135: Thomas Stearns
p 137: Cary Grant
p 139: George Foreman
p 141: Chico
p 143: Dr. Hawley Harvey Crippen (the Captain of the SS *Montrose* alerted Scotland Yard that the suspect was on board)
p 145: Yuri Gagarin
p 147: Onion
p 149: They contain 25% air
p 151: Greta Garbo
p 153: Moscow
p 155: Louis Le Prince (1888)
p 157: A smack
p 159: International Orange
p 161: The car radio
p 163: Silence
p 165: Erle Stanley Gardner
p 167: Leo Baekeland (1909)
p 169: The automobile
p 171: Edgar Rice Burroughs
p 173: The key of F